How to Write
REPORTS

A GUIDE FOR GRADES 6-9

Randy Larson

 J. Weston Walch, Publisher
Portland, Maine

Users' Guide
to
Walch Reproducible Books

As part of our general effort to provide educational materials which are as practical and economical as possible, we have designated this publication a "reproducible book." The designation means that purchase of the book includes purchase of the right to limited reproduction of all pages on which this symbol appears:

Here is the basic Walch policy: We grant to individual purchasers of this book the right to make sufficient copies of reproducible pages for use by all students of a single teacher. This permission is limited to a single teacher, and does not apply to entire schools or school systems, so institutions purchasing the book should pass the permission on to a single teacher. Copying of the book or its parts for resale is prohibited.

Any questions regarding this policy or requests to purchase further reproduction rights should be addressed to:

Permissions Editor
J. Weston Walch, Publisher
P.O. Box 658
Portland, ME 04104-0658

—*J. Weston Walch, Publisher*

1   2   3   4   5   6   7   8   9   10

ISBN 0-8251-1782-8

Contents

Part 1: Teaching Guide

Part 2: Reproducible Student Lessons and Activities

Chapter 1: Finding a Topic

Chapter 2: Using the Library

Chapter 3: Gathering Information

Chapter 4: Writing the Report

Section 1: Writing the Lead

Section 2: Writing Introductions

Section 3: Using Transitions

To the Teacher

This book was written for teachers who assign reports and for students who must complete those assignments. The book does *not* propose an "easy" solution to the task. Report writing is beyond "easy" and should be approached with no nonsense and no illusions.

That does not mean report writing can't be interesting or even intriguing. That does not mean students/parents/teachers have to be bored out of their wits when they hear the word *report*. But it does mean that some real work will be done by all involved, and that some real feelings or accomplishment will belong to those who see the project through.

For those who doubt the value of writing reports, take note: Report writing runs the gamut of Bloom's *Taxonomy* and a couple of other "onomies." Deciding on a topic requires knowledge, comprehension, analysis, synthesis, application, and evaluation skills. Focusing a topic (narrowing), gathering information, organizing that information, and writing the report demand that the student use every learning tool in his or her kit; and when the job is finished, the pride, self-assurance, and sense of achievement are immediate—no need to wait till the grades are posted.

This text was designed to help students and teachers win the mental marathon called report writing and includes lessons on every phase of the project. It begins with an explanation of what a report is and isn't; it offers lessons on choosing/narrowing a topic, using the library and its new technologies, gathering and organizing information from many different sources, and writing the actual report (lead and introduction, body, and conclusion); it supplies a model, including notecards and outline, for students who want to see what a finished report should look like; *and* it provides a list of 500 topics to quell the question "What's there to write about?"

But before the work can begin, it is essential that you—the teacher, the inspirer—know the answers to two elemental questions that always crop up like quack grass and won't go away:

1. What is a report?
2. What is plagiarism?

A report is an account of the facts—not the facts as applied to a thesis, not the facts as they support a particular viewpoint or position, but the facts as they are without qualification or interpretation. A report can be something as direct as an account of the events at a volleyball game. Or it can tell what happened during a trial or a war. A report can explain how cannons fire, or how kidneys function, or how a cuckoo comes out of a clock. A report could teach the reader how to play rugby or checkers or hide-and-seek. A report *cannot* propose what should be done about people who cheat at checkers, nor can it defend the position that rugby is the toughest sport in the world. There is no argument in a report, no fight at all.

But how do you present the facts as they are without being there to see how the kidney works or how rugby is played? You read, of course, and report back to those who haven't read. You interview, you watch films and listen to tapes and speeches, and you record what you find out from many different sources and write it all down. But if you weren't there to get the facts, whose facts are they, and how do you tactfully acknowledge their owners?

Plagiarism and truthful reporting run neck and neck in a race that is often hard to call. After all, isn't most of the information any of us has a borrowed commodity? Were any of us there at Plymouth Rock when the Pilgrims rowed ashore? How do we know they rowed? How many of us have read the journals and letters and legal documents of these people? When we or our students report on such subjects, shouldn't every line contain a credit notation for using other people's research?

The answer of course is that such bookkeeping would kill any report because the eye won't tolerate the harassment. A solution is to include a list of "sources consulted" at the end of a report, along with a list of the sources from which specific information has been borrowed, and to note the author and page number within the body of the report when a quote, fact, or concept is used that unquestionably belongs to someone else, and let it go at that.

We're not talking here about the student who runs to the library and copies something from an encyclopedia. That piece of thievery should be torn asunder and the thief should be dealt with harshly. But then, what good is assigning a one-source "encyclopedia report" to a middle school or junior high student anyway? The student often sees the assignment as either a joke or a punishment, and takes the fastest way out. Right or wrong, teachers' motives as well as students' plagiarisms have caught the attention of many educators who feel that there has to be a better way.

The better way is to teach kids how to research and write reports in such a way that they learn to explore, to investigate subjects that interest them, and to gather bits of information from several different sources (perspectives) and build the stuff into a sensible structure. This can be done without plagiarism, without creating a mishmash of loud opinions, and without becoming bored.

That's why this book was written. You can use the exercises to take a student sequentially from the first step of finding a topic to the final steps of writing a good report. And students can learn how to create intelligent nonfiction along the way. It is the author's hope that this is exactly what happens.

Randy Larson
English Teacher
Burn High School
Burns, Wyoming

Teaching Guide

Like any writing, report writing is a process. It requires time, effort, and a tremendous amount of perseverance from both students and teachers. To reduce the strain, this guide provides goals, objectives, and teaching tips for each chapter in the hopes that you can adapt the material to suit your students and your strengths as an educator.

Chapter 1: Finding a Topic

Goals: Students will know what a report is and why they will write reports.

Students will understand the difference between a report topic and an opinion.

Students will learn how to choose and narrow a topic for a report.

Students will learn how to find a specific angle on a report topic.

Objectives: Students will . . .

1. Identify the five *W's* in a mini-report.
2. Use the five *W's* to write a mini-report.
3. Distinguish between statements of fact and statements of opinion.
4. Write specific questions to further investigate a subject.
5. Select the most appropriate topic out groups of three.
6. Write specific topic titles based on broad subjects.

Tips: Students could bring in report cards and weather reports.

Students could bring a collage of magazine pictures arranged from general to specific: VEHICLE,

                         CAR,

                                  SPORTS CAR,

                                     etc.

Students could cut out the topic title of reports found in magazines: *Scholastic, Time,* etc.

Chapter 2: Using the Library

Goals: Students will understand how a library is organized.

Students will learn where different kinds of information are stored.

Students will learn how to use the tools of the library (card catalog, microfiche, electronic readers, and so on).

Objectives: Students will . . .

1. Match books to Dewey decimal categories.

2. Write library cards from examples given.

3. Alphabetize and number-order lists of titles, authors, and subjects.

4. Name the locations in the library where various kinds of books would be found.

5. Write out entries from the *Readers' Guide.*

6. Align books with the appropriate drawer in the card catalog.

Tips: Book hunts (like treasure hunts) can help kids get acquainted with the library.

Odd One Out—teams compete to find the oddest facts (almanacs, digests, dictionaries, etc.).

Field trips—take kids to a big public library.

Guest presenter—ask the city librarian or a researcher to speak to the class.

Kids could build their own library, categorizing books they've made themselves or that you've gleaned from a friend's rummage sale.

Chapter 3: Gathering Information

Goals: Students will learn how to glean information from sources.

Students will learn how to organize information.

Objectives: Students will . . .

1. Identify and write subheads for articles, paragraphs, and lists using devices such as bullets and bold type.

2. List details taken from paragraphs on notecards.

3. Prioritize notes into an outline using a prewritten structure or framework.

Tips: Students could listen to stories of their classmates and take notes.

Students could put a jumble of objects into categories according to criteria such as "use," "color," and "price" (to teach grouping skills).

Students could put family members in categories, then list the details about each member.

Students could use skimming to speed-read a piece out of a magazine or book and write the most details in the least time.

Chapter 4: Writing the Report

Section 1: Writing the Lead

Goals: Students will learn what makes a good lead as opposed to a poor one.

Students will understand the need for a good lead in a report.

Objectives: Students will . . .

1. Identify good leads out of several in a list.
2. Identify three types of leads.
3. Write a story lead, a quote lead, and a question lead.

Tips: Students can cut leads from newspapers.

Students can tape leads from nightly newscasts.

Students can write leads for bizarre stories about classmates.

Students can create a "group lead" by writing a detail on a piece of paper, then handing it to the next student.

Section 2: Writing Introductions

Goals: Students will understand the need for a solid introduction.

Students will learn the difference betewen an introduction and a lead.

Students will learn to write introductions for a variety of report topics.

Objectives: Students will . . .

1. Write introductions according to the models and guidelines set forth: from the general subject to the specific topic of a report.
2. Write a lead combined with an introduction.

Section 3: Using Transitions

Goals: Students will understand the importance of moving through a piece of information according to a determined pattern: chronological or spatial.

Objectives: Students will . . .

1. Identify spatial and chronological transitions in pieces of writing and from lists.
2. Write paragraphs using time transitions.
3. Write paragraphs using space transitions.
4. Write paragraphs using both time and space transitions on the same subject.

Section 4: Summarizing

Goals: Students will understand the reason for summaries. Students will learn to write summaries and combine them to make a mini-report.

Objectives: Students will . . .

1. Write one-line summaries in telegram form.

2. Write one-line summaries from a list of details.

3. Write brief summaries of books and movies.

4. Write brief summaries from nonfiction paragraphs.

5. Write brief summaries and then combine them into a longer summary paragraph.

Tips: Point out to the students that the summaries of summaries that they did on pages 151–152 are actually paraphrases, which will be coming up next.

Section 5: Paraphrasing

Goals: Students will understand the difference between a paraphrase and a summary.

Students will learn how to avoid plagiarism by paraphrasing.

Students will learn how to transform bits of information into complete paragraphs.

Objectives: Students will . . .

1. Write several paraphrases on a variety of subjects taken from sample paragraphs.

2. Write paraphrases based on a list of details.

3. Write paragraphs based on notes provided.

Tips: **Transforming** is the process of turning notes into sentences—a good way to learn paraphrasing.

Students could paraphrase each other from a list of details.

Section 6: Using Quotes

Goals: Students will learn the importance of using direct quotes in a report.

Students will learn the difference between a "good" quote and a "poor" one.

Students will learn how to make a separate notecard for a quote borrowed during research.

Students will learn how to write quotes into the body of text in a report.

Students will understand that direct quotes must be credited to avoid plagiarism.

Objectives: Students will . . .

1. Identify "good" from "poor" or weak quotes.

2. Write quotes onto notecards, including the source.

3. Write quotes as if they were going into the text by including the speaker's name, occupation, and the word *said.*

4. Write quotes as if they were going into the text, giving proper credit for the source.

Tips: Using actual notecards should help in this exercise.

Students could use newspapers brought to class, or TV interviews or talk show interviews to fill notecards with quotes.

Students could take a piece of solid nonfiction and invent quotes and insert them in the copy.

Note: Using notecards is one way of recording information for a report. Suggesting a notebook or some other method might be effective for some students at this point.

Section 7: Crediting Information

Goals: Students will learn the seriousness of plagiarism.

Students will learn which is public and which is specific, creditable information.

Students will learn how to credit a fact in the MLA style.

Objectives: Students will . . .

1. Identify public information as opposed to specific information.

2. Credit specific facts in sample paragraphs using the MLA style.

Tips: Students could brainstorm and make a list on the board of things "everybody" knows.

Students could come up with a list of different kinds of plagiarism: concepts, ideas, theories.

Students could talk about their feelings and attitudes toward thieves.

Students could discuss how they would react if someone turned in an essay or report copied word for word from them.

Section 8: Writing Conclusions

Goals: Students will understand why some reports are failures.

Students will learn what a general opinion statement is.

Students will learn how to write general opinion statements.

Students will learn how to write conclusion paragraphs.

Objectives: Students will . . .

1. Identify general opinion statements from a list of opinions and find these statements in given paragraphs.

2. Write general opinion statements of their own.

3. Write conclusions for well-known subjects such as "Martin Luther King."

Tips: Have students read some conclusions of articles in magazines or at the end of news stories on TV or in newspapers.

Read a news story without an ending and watch the reaction.

Section 9: Reveal the Source

Goals: Students will learn how to list sources on a "Sources Consulted" page.

Objectives: Students will read the two pages showing the examples of different kinds of entries.

Tips: Students could make a list of five sources on a general topic.

Answer Key

Chapter 1: Finding a Topic

Show and Tell

WHO:	teenagers
WHAT:	making maple syrup
WHERE:	New England, U.S.A.
WHEN:	springtime
WHY:	to make money

First Report

WHO:	Scientists Roberta Bustin and Everett Gibson
WHAT:	discovered that moon rocks contain hydrogen from which water can be made
WHERE:	in a lab
WHEN:	recently
WHY:	to aid in space travel—we can build a moon base

This Is News!

POSSIBLE MINI-REPORT:

Mikhail Gorbachev visited the United States on December 7, 1988, traveling to the United Nations Building in New York. While there he announced to the world that the Soviet Union would be withdrawing 500,000 troops from military bases around the world.

Do It Again!

POSSIBLE SHORT REPORT:

Every day across the United States, 4,000 teens drop out of school, a total of approximately 700,000 per year. Some are gifted students who are bored; others leave because of poor academic skills, behavior problems, poor self-image, or a sincere belief that they don't need school to succeed.

And Once More

Peter Diamond, from Tunkhannock, Pennsylvania, recently designed a removable passenger compartment for jetliners. The theory is that the compartment would be ejected from the body of the plane in case of severe mechanical problems and let to earth by parachute. The plane would then land in a desert or ocean using autopilot controls. The device would save hundreds of lives each year.

Fact Finding

1. O	3. O	5. O	7. F	9. O
2. F	4. O	6. F	8. F	

Fact Practice	1. F	3. F	5. F	7. O	9. O
	2. O	4. F	6. O	8. F	10. F

You Try It!   **POSSIBLE QUESTIONS:**

1. How do you train a show dog?

2. How much of Canada has snow year-round?

3. What will happen to the aborigines of Australia in years to come?

4. How do canaries "sing"?

5. Why does a cobra have a hood?

6. Where did algebra come from?

7. What is silver salt?

8. Why do marshmallows float?

Get Curious   **POSSIBLE QUESTIONS:**

1. CLOWNS

    a. Is there such a thing as clown college?

    b. How much does a clown earn in a year?

    c. Do rodeo clowns die young?

    d. Do clowns get a pension?

    e. Do clowns take themselves seriously?

2. FAT/MUSCLE

    a. Is there such a thing as having too much muscle?

    b. How do you lose fat and keep your muscles?

    c. How often does a person need to work out to lose a pound per week?

    d. When do you know you're too fat?

    e. How do steroids affect muscle growth?

Stay Curious   **POSSIBLE QUESTIONS:**

1. MODEL

    a. Who is the oldest living fashion model?

    b. Which is the best modeling school in the world?

    c. Why do people want to become models?

    d. How much do top models earn?

    e. Who designs the latest in women's fashion?

2. FUTURE

    a. How is time measured in outer space?

    b. Has anyone ever traveled into the future and come back to tell about it?

    c. Would you come back younger than when you left for the future?

    d. Could you change things today that would affect your life in the future?

    e. What things would be impossible to change no matter how long you were gone into the future?

Keep Asking   **POSSIBLE QUESTIONS:**

HOMELESS

1. Who exactly are the homeless among us?

2. What do they live on?

3. Where do they go during the day?

4. When did this problem become so widespread?

5. Why are they out there on the streets?

CASTLES

1. Who built the first castle in history?

2. What problems did castle-building present to the carpenters and masons who built these structures?

3. Where are the most castles located?

4. When did castles become obsolete?

5. Why did people build castles in the first place?

More Questions   **POSSIBLE QUESTIONS:**

STEREO SYSTEMS

1. What is the stereo system, exactly?

2. Who invented the first stereo?

3. When was the first stereo invented?

4. Why is stereo sound so much better than normal sound?

UNIVERSITY LIFE

1. Who decides what is taught at a university?

2. When was the first university built?

3. What were early universities like?

4. Why do you need a college degree to do most jobs today?

HOMEWORK

1. Who benefits most from homework?

2. What is the purpose of homework?

3. When should homework *not* be assigned?

4. Where is the best place to do homework?

Drawing the Line   CANNIBALS: "When trapped and starving . . . "

MAIL-ORDER CATALOGS: "Sixty years ago, . . . "

SHEEP: "Many teens make money . . . "

PERFUME: "Some people are . . . "

COMIC STRIPS: "Political comic . . . "

ROCK STARS: "Rock concerts have . . . "

COCKROACHES: "Cockroaches eat . . . "

MOON: "The moon is the subject . . . "

MUSIC VIDEOS: "Music videos are . . . "

SUGAR: "Babies have a natural . . . "

BREAKFAST CEREAL: no match available

POISONS: no match available

Too Big,
Parts II & III   **TOPICS TOO BIG ARE:**

Group 1. The mammals of Canada

Group 2. Computers around the world

Group 3. World hunger

Group 4. Nuclear energy

Group 5. Presidents of the United States

Group 6. Explorers of the ancient world

Group 7. Tourism in Australia

Group 8. European painters

Group 9. Solar energy

Group 10. Injustice around the world

Be Exact

POSSIBLE ANSWERS:

Triangle 2 . . . How to maintain a racing bike

Triangle 3 . . . Drug peddling

. . . Drug peddling and its effect on teenagers

Monsters of the Midway

POSSIBLE TOPIC TITLES:

1. Professional athletes experience as much stress as any business executive.

2. Traveling by airplane is proven to be the safest way of getting there.

3. Teenage drug addicts can get serious help from support groups.

4. The trick to becoming a teenage magician is finding someone to show you the ropes.

More Monsters

POSSIBLE TOPIC TITLES:

1. Expensive jewelry is a good investment of your hard-earned money.

2. Many very sensible people have claimed they've seen UFOs.

3. It takes more than luck to win at most video games.

4. Earning money is a problem for teens who want to keep up their grades.

Still More Monsters

POSSIBLE TOPIC TITLES:

1. Junk food is any food that does nothing for you nutritionally.

2. Horror stories began when the first group of humans sat around the first fire and stared out into the night.

3. Diving for sunken treasure requires a treasure chest full of money to buy the necessary equipment.

4. Dinosaur fossils found in Wyoming and Colorado tell us that the Great Plains were once under water.

5. Lifeguard training can be grueling.

6. Few foods are better for you than dried grapes, otherwise known as raisins.

Weed 'Em Out   **TOPICS TOO SMALL ARE:**

Group 1. How to change your cat's litter box

Group 2. Two ways to hold a paintbrush

Group 3. How to drink from a drinking fountain

Group 4. How to release a ladybug

Keep Weedin'   **TOPICS TOO SMALL ARE:**

Group 1. My trip to the dentist

Group 2. How to play the autoharp . . .

Group 3. My favorite kind of cheese

Group 4. How to hold your fork

Group 5. The day my pet turtle disappeared

Just Write I

1. TB	2. TB	3. TB	4. TS	5. JR
TS	JR	JR	JR	TB
JR	TS	TS	TB	TS

Just Write II

1. TB	2. JR	3. TS	4. TB	5. TS
JR	TB	TB	TS	JR
TS	TS	JR	JR	TB

Chapter 2: Using the Library

Code Match

1. 900	5. 300	9. 700	13. 900	17. 400
2. 900	6. 000–099	10. 700	14. 200	18. 100
3. 800	7. 900	11. 900	15. 400	19. 000–099
4. 500	8. 600	12. 900	16. 300	20. 200

The Unscrambling

1. 900	5. Correct	9. Correct	13. 300	17. Correct
2. 500	6. 600	10. Correct	14. Correct	18. 500
3. 700	7. Correct	11. Correct	15. 100	
4. 600	8. Correct	12. Correct	16. Correct	

Write In

1. Language
2. Language
3. History/
   Biography
4. Religion
5. Applied
   Science
6. Psychology
7. History/
   Biography
8. Literature
9. Social Sciences
10. Religion
11. History/
    Biography
12. Science
13. Fine Arts
14. History/
    Biography
15. General Works
16. Science
17. History/
    Biography
18. Language

Guide *Use*

RAVENS

title: The Raven's Feast
author: B. Heinrich
illustrations: yes
magazine: *Natural History*
page numbers: 44–51
month/year of magazine: February 1989

HAIRSTYLING

title: The Bob Is Back
author: C. Straley
illustrations: yes
magazine: *Parents*
volume no.: 64
page numbers: 92–94
month/year of magazine:
    January 1989

Quiz Time

1. January
2. February
3. March
4. April
5. May
6. June
7. July
8. August
9. September
10. October
11. November
12. December
13. illustrated
14. bi-monthly
15. bibliography
16. portrait
17. supplement
18. introduction
19. continued
20. monthly
21. volume
22. Summer
23. revised

The Right Source

1. 1, 2, 4, 5
2. 8
3. 1, 7
4. 1, 2, 3, 10
5. 1, 2, 7, 9
6. 1, 2, 3, 10
7. 6
8. 10
9. 2, 4, 6
10. 1, 2, 3, 7, 10

Out of Line

1. 1
2. 10
3. 14
4. 3
5. 4
6. 2
7. 6
8. 9
9. 5
10. 7
11. 8
12. 13
13. 11
14. 12

Alphabet Skills

BA–BE: 2, 3, 4, 5, 9
BI–BK: none
BL–BO: 8, 6
BR–BY: 10, 7, 1

Orders, Orders, Orders!

38 Botany	40 Buffalo	1 Abortion
31 Beagles	10 Apples	24 Automobiles
41 Bulimia	25 Baby-sitters	18 Aspirin
19 Assassins	27 Bananas	6 Anorexia
14 Aristotle	28 Baseball	13 Architects
26 Bacon	29 Basketball	35 Biology
15 Arizona	30 Battles	33 Bells
16 Art	4 Amphibians	21 Athletes
17 Asia	2 Acid Rain	20 Astronauts
34 Bible	3 Adolescents	8 Anthropology
39 Bridges	37 Blood	9 Ants
22 Atmosphere	42 Business	5 Anatomy
7 Antarctica	36 Birds	12 Archaeology
11 Arab Countries	23 Atomic Bomb	32 Bees

Fill in the Card

```
                Fire! How Do They Fight It?
628.9   Dean, Anabel
D               Fire! How Do They Fight It?/by Anabel Dean; ill.
                with photos. Westminister, c 1978.

                112 p.; ill., photos

                1. Fire Prevention    2. Firefighting

                I. Title

                A history of firefighting, covering techniques
                for combatting city fires, forest fires, and
                airport fires.
```

```
                Look to This Day
920     Campion, Nardi R.
Gui             Look to This Day/by Nardi R. Campion; ill. with
                photos. Little, Brown, c 1965.

                508 p.: ill., photos
                1. Medicine/Biog

                I. Title

                The Life and education of one of America's first
                female physicians: Connie Guion, M.D.
```

Do It Yourself

SUBJECT CARD

```
            FRIENDSHIP
177    Richards, Arlene K.
R          Boy Friends, Girl Friends, Just Friends/
       by Arlene K. Richards; ill. with photos.
       Atheneum, c. 1079.

           1.55 p.: ill., photos

       1. Friendship

       An explanation of the pleasures, pains, and
       responsibilities of friendship in the high
       school years.
```

AUTHOR CARD

```
       Richards, Arlene K.
177        Boy Friends, Girl Friends, Just Friends/by
R      Arlene K. Richards; ill. with photos.
       Atheneum, 1979

           155 p.: ill., photos

       1. Friendship

       An explanation of the pleasures, pains, and
       responsibilities of friendship in the high
       school years.
```

TITLE CARD

```
       Boy Friends, Girl Friends, Just Friends
177    Richards, Arlene K.
R          Boy Friends, Girl Friends, Just Friends/by
       Arlene K. Richards; ill. with photos.
       Atheneum, 1979.

           155 p.: ill., photos

       1. Friendship

       I. Title

       An explanation of the pleasures, pains, and
       responsibilities of friendship in the high
       school years.
```

"Numberize"!

Correct order of books: 200, 220.1, 220.9, 242,
248.4, 261.7, 291, 291.63,
292, 335.4, 337.8,
338, 338.1, 340.023, 341, 341.13,
342.522, 346.01, 351.009,
353.03, 353.5, 355,
364.973, 365.973

Last Step					
1. A	5. C	9. C	13. A	17. B	21. C
2. C	6. B	10. A	14. A	18. B	22. C
3. B	7. B	11. C	15. B	19. B	
4. A	8. C	12. C	16. B	20. C	

Next of Kin

Correct order of books:		
	1. 6	6. 2
	2. 3	7. 10
	3. 1	8. 5
	4. 8	9. 4
	5. 9	10. 7

Everything in Its Place

1. 3	6. 4	11. 8
2. 5	7. 8	12. 3
3. 7	8. 3	13. 8
4. 6	9. 8	14. 2
5. 4	10. 7	15. 8

Chapter 3: Gathering Information

Watch for Bullets

Subtitle:	Conflicting Interpretations
Bullet 1.	Intent to plagiarize is irrelevant at most schools, and, in any case, lack of intent is very difficult to prove.
Bullet 2.	Claiming "I only copied one sentence here or one paragraph there" is no defense.
Bullet 3.	"But I put it in my own words" is also no defense.
3ullet 4.	You must acknowledge every appearance of borrowed material.
Bullet 5.	Whether or not a source is copyrighted is also immaterial.

Zero In

Bullet 2.	State a hypothesis.
Bullet 3.	Perform an experiment.
Bullet 4.	Other scientists repeat the experiment.
Bullet 5.	Form a conclusion.

**Food for
Thought**   BREAKFAST: scrambled eggs and ham, pancakes, waffles, French
                           toast, wheat toast

              DINNER: jumbo shrimp, sirloin steak, baked trout, braised
                        duck, roast leg of lamb, grilled pork chops

              DESSERT: chocolate pie, ice cream, cake, apple pie, pineapple
                         sundae

Skim It!   Any item on menu

**Subheads,
Where Are You?**   Subhead 1.   Fundraising for You and Your Organization

               Subhead 2.   Planning Your Fundraiser

               Subhead 3.   Selling Door to Door

               Subhead 4.   Hard Work Pays Off

**More
Subheads**   Circled words in paragraph   1. "The morning of . . ."
               "   "   "   "   2. "Some people say . . . "
               "   "   "   "   3. "The first snowfall . . . "

               Subhead 1.   The Revolutionary War Begins

               Subhead 2.   The Mail Order Catalog

               Subhead 3.   The First Snowfall

**Do It
Yourself**   List Subhead.   Traveling by Plane

               List Subhead.   Visiting Hospital Patients

**Find the
Subhead**   Paragraph 1: Subhead. Starting a Service Business

              Paragraph 2: Subhead. Good Study Habits

**Skimming
Practice**   Paragraph 1: Subhead. Slavery Starts the War

                  1st sentence. Among the many reasons for Civil War,
                                slavery was the most obvious.

              Paragraph 2: Subhead. Abolitionists Fuel the Fire

                  1st sentence. Citizens who were violently against
                                slavery were called "abolitionists."

              Paragraph 3: Subhead. The War Begins

                  1st sentence. Finally, in December of 1860, South
                                Carolina broke from the United States.

Good Notes   2. 27 million acres burned off
3. carbon dioxide level is rising
4. sun's heat trapped = global warming

Keep Skimming   Card 2: Subhead. Rewards of Exercise

Details: 1. calms you
2. increases blood flow
3. appetite for sweets and salts decreases
4. sleep better

Card 3: Subhead. Cautions About Exercise

Details: 1. don't overwork
2. stop with any pain
3. start slowly
4. rest often
5. gradually increase workouts

**From Bullets
to Notes**   Card 1: Subhead. Handling Stress Creatively

Details: 1. Realize some things you can't control.
2. Don't brood.
3. Seek ways to help get through stress.
    a. Moving: get brochures & info from new town.
4. Do positive things.

Card 2: Subhead. Think Positively

Details: 1. Don't dwell on negative.
2. Make situation work for you, not against you.
3. You can control your thoughts.
4. Remember: You haven't changed, the situation has.

More Notes   Card 1: CHILDHOOD

1. Born February, 1809, Hodgenville, KY (poor)
2. Two years old moved to Knob Creek, KY
3. At age seven (1817) moved to Indiana
    a. lived in three-sided lean-to
4. Mother died following year

Card 2: CHILDHOOD

1. Young boy (aged nine) did chores, worked hard
    a. learned to read and write
    b. borrowed books from miles away
2. At 17 he saw first city: New Orleans
    a. saw slavery first-hand, close up

Take Note   Card 1: *Climate*

1. wet, rainy winters
2. heavy snow in mountain foothills
3. hot, dry eastern plains
   —grow much fruit and grain

Card 2: *Natural Resources*

1. Mt. Rainier—14,000 feet
2. Columbia River—drops 1,200 feet over 7 dams before meeting ocean—produces more hydroelectric power than any other river in U.S.
3. Huge forests
4. Good harbors
5. Lots of parks—3 national, 12 state—& historical sites

Card 3: *Economy*

1. Huge labor market—4 million people/60,000 Native Americans
2. Many industries—aircraft, computers, logging, fishing, banking, mining, farming
   —$66 billion in foreign trade
   —500 computer software companies
   —Boeing Aircraft—employs 60,000

Fill in the Cards   Card 1: Definition:

1. waves produced by magnetron
   —invented 1940/Raytheon Corporation
2. too fast for eye to see
3. used for radar, then accidentally found could cook food
   —first oven in 1952/6 ft. tall

Card 2: Function:

1. spin water molecules end over end 2.4 billion times per second
2. vibration of molecules causes friction
3. friction makes heat; food is cooked

Card 3: Uses:

1. cancer tumors destroyed with microwaves
   —tumors don't have way to heal themselves (no blood)

Picture These
Notes
   Card 1: Explanation:
      1. Photography uses light and chemicals
      2. Silver salt gets darker with light
      3. Put silver salt on film, put object between film and light source, and object is outlined on film

   Card 2: Famous Photographers:
      1. Niepce—1st photography—1826
      2. Daguerre—used mercury vapor to develop clearer pictures
      3. Mathew Brady—Civil War—made photography important to public
      4. Margaret Bourke-White—1940's—brought WWII into public's eyes

   Card 3: Getting Started:
      1. Understand light/shadow relationship
      2. Find interesting subjects, creative angles
      3. Get sturdy, practical 35mm camera
      4. Take photo course—school/college
      5. Read books, magazines, journals
      6. Find camera lovers and talk—local newspaper photographer
      7. Take lots, lots, lots of photos

Make a
Plan

  I. Definition—Microwaves
    A. Can't be seen by human eye
    B. Generated by "magnetron"

  II. Function
    A. Spin water molecules within food
      1. 2.4 billion times per second
    B. Vibration of molecules causes friction
    C. Friction causes heat

  III. Uses
    A. Originally for radar
    B. Cooking food
    C. Burning out cancer tumors
      1. Tumors can't heal—then "die"

Make Another
Plan

 Washington State

  I. Climate
    A. Wet/rainy winters on west coast
    B. Cool/snowy autumns in foothills
    C. Hot/dry summers in eastern plains

   II. Natural Resources
      A. Big mountains like Mt. Rainier
         1. mountain climbing/sightseeing
         2. mountains provide drinking water from heavy snowfall

      B. Columbia River runs 1,200 miles
         1. most hydroelectric power in U.S.

      C. Excellent ocean harbors

      D. Giant forests

      E. Parks—3 national, 12 state—& historical sites

  III. Economy
      A. Manufacturing
         1. aircraft—Boeing Aircraft employs 60,000
         2. computer software—500 software companies

      B. Farming (fruit/grains), logging, fishing

      C. Industry—mining

      D. $66 billion in foreign trade (mostly to Japan)

Chapter 4: Writing the Report

Section 1: Writing the Lead

What's What?

1. Qt	3. Qn	5. Qt	7. Qn	9. Qt
2. S	4. S	6. Qn	8. Qn	10. S

X *It*

2, 4, 6, 7, 8

New, Improved Leads

1. "A dog can be smart, strong, dependable, and extremely trainable, but nothing—I mean nothing—compares with the brains and brawn of a seeing-eye dog."

2. Does having your face covered thick with makeup, keeping a constant smile on your face, having people watching every move you make, and being pressured to perform for huge crowds sound like fun?

More Improved Leads

1. "There is nothing in modern society that captures the heart, mind, and hopes of teenagers today like the electronic dreambox—television."

2. When it's all said and done, and the last Christmas gift has been purchased, do you feel an empty sensation when you reach into your pocket or purse for a $5 bill?

3. How could she think he wouldn't be hurt? He'd bought her everything—a diamond ring, clothes, a poodle, and of course the Corvette, but she said that wasn't enough. She said she wanted him rather than "things." Jim stormed out of the apartment down to the curb where her Corvette was parked. He dug out his spare key, started the engine, and drove away. His last view of Sally was her face framed in the kitchen window as he roared off into the night.

Do All Three

1. (Quote Lead)

   "Nothing discourages me more than to see healthy, intelligent people take up a habit that will very likely become their executioner."

2. (Question Lead)

   If you were told that doing a particular thing would almost surely lead to a long and painful death, would you do it?

3. (Story Lead)

   She felt the needle going in but didn't cry out. The nurse was gentle and said things like, "I'm sorry about this." But with cancer you take what they give you, and if life comes from an intravenous needle full of anticancer drugs, then so be it. She never dreamed her senior year would end like this. "Cancer of the throat," they'd said. "Probably caused by smoking."

Section 2: Writing Introductions

Do It Yourself

War is one of humankind's greatest tragedies. And one of the worst ever fought was the American Civil War, which is remembered for its terrible, bloody moments. The battle of Gettysburg and the burning of the great city of Atlanta are just two events that no American can ever forget. But probably the most famous event was the surrender of the Southern army at Appomattox Court House when General Lee handed his battle sword to General Grant.

Write an Introduction

Humans have always had a keen interest in animals. We have hunted them, trained them to perform, and made pets out of many species. One of the most popular species for use as a pet is the common cat. And one of the best-known and best-liked breeds of all cats is the exotic Siamese, with its distinct coloring and low, mournful meow.

On Your Own

Education is important to all people, especially youngsters, so parents often choose to send their children to preschools and nurseries where reading and writing and other skills are taught. But often youngsters can learn as much at home as they can at school if someone is there to teach them. That's where the television can be very useful, because several educational programs are offered every day from early morning to late afternoon for youngsters who are at home. One of the best of these is the famous *Sesame Street* with its cast of characters such as Big Bird and Cookie Monster.

Another Introduction

America's amusement parks are a worldwide attraction drawing people from all walks of life, from every country of the world, from every age group. Parks such as Disneyland, Coney Island in New York, and Great America bring pleasure to millions of people each year. People visit these places to relax, to play games, and to take rides on machines that send them splashing through water or soaring through the air. The most feared and sought-after of all these rides is the roller coaster, a snakelike creature that hurtles people skyward only to pull them back to earth at terrific, death-defying speeds.

The Great Combination

John tried to look away but couldn't pull his eyes from the horrible scene—a creature with one eye dripping blood who was slowly crawling toward a group of campers sitting around the fire beside a lake. At the first crunch of bone John gasped and grabbed the arm of his chair. He was delightfully terrified.

Being thrilled and shocked has always been a main reason for people going to the movies. In the early days of film, cop shows and murder mysteries kept moviegoers glued to their seats. Then monster movies and space horror films scared us to the bone. But no type of thrill-and-chill movie has gripped the mind of movie-watchers more than the cold-blooded horror films of the past 20 years.

Another Great Combo

"I never dreamed something so small could be so deadly or so terrifying," said Wanda Burkett, a ranch wife in Tucson, Arizona.

People like Wanda have been terrified by a vast number of creatures that have roamed the earth since life began. In the early days it was the dinosaur and saber-toothed tiger that people feared. And smaller creatures like snakes, scorpions, and insects crept into dwellings and pumped deadly poison into their victims. One of the most feared throughout recorded time has been the black widow spider, a deadly creature that can kill a human 3,200 times larger than itself.

One More Combo   What's the best way we know of to go from one place to another?

Some would say that the best way to travel is by car, and it would be hard to disagree—a car is private and fairly fast, and it gives the rider freedom to go anywhere within reason. Others would say a horse because a horse will get you where you want to go and won't pollute the atmosphere. Many more would claim that the airplane is by far the safest and fastest way to travel that exists today. But there is still another choice, a machine that many believe will be the main source of power in the cities of the future—the bicycle, a machine that is fast, lightweight, portable, dependable, and fuel-free.

Section 3: Using Transitions

All in Order   The movie I saw was called *Crazy People*. It began with the main character, played by Dudley Moore, getting sent to a mental institution for having very weird advertising ideas. Then Dudley fell in love with a beautiful girl. Meanwhile his strange advertisements were catching on, and he was teaching his new friends at the institution to write them too. They get in all kinds of trouble. Finally at the end Dudley helps all his friends escape and they start their own ad company.

Order Up!   All answers, 1–18, are **T**.

Find the Time   Paragraph 1.   Transitions that should be circled:
FIRST, SECOND, NEXT, THEN, FINALLY

Paragraph 2.   Transitions that should be circled:
TO BEGIN, THEN, AFTER, FOLLOWING

Paragraph A.   Correct Sentence Order: 1, 2, 4, 3

Paragraph B.   Correct Sentence Order: 4, 2, 3, 1, 5

Paragraph 1.   first
next
then
finally

Paragraph 2.   then
eventually
since

Write It!   *Paragraph 1*

Cleaning a dirty bedroom can be a nasty job that will go faster if you're organized. To start with, remove everything that belongs someplace else: Your dirty clothes go in the hamper, your sister's curling iron goes back to her room, and your tennis racket goes in the hall closet. Once that's done, organize everything that's left. Now you're ready to actually do some cleaning—vacuum the floor, dust the shelves, and make the bed. Finally, relax and put your feet up.

Paragraph 2

An electric skillet is an appliance that can take the place of a stove. It begins to heat up when the main dial is turned to a specific temperature setting; the dial acts as a switch that closes the gap in the electrical circuit running through the cord. Electricity flows through a coil built into the bottom of the pan, very similar to the coil you often see in an electric oven. Then as the coil heats, a small sensor in the dial records the temperature of the pan. When the temperature starts to rise, the sensor shuts off the flow of the current temporarily in order to keep the temperature at the level set by the dial.

Space Words in Action

At the top of my imaginary sundae sits the world's fattest red cherry—about the size of a grapefruit. Just beneath this red beauty lies a one-foot layer of chocolate fudge. Under the fudge rests a gigantic scoop of ice cream—as big as a hot air balloon. Around the mound of ice cream hangs a heavy fringe of whipped cream, and at the bottom of the fancy glass dish lie six tasty banana slices.

Transitions used: at the top
beneath
under
around
at the bottom

Time or Space

1. T	8. T	15. S	22. T	29. T
2. T	9. T	16. S	23. S	30. S
3. S	10. S	17. S	24. T	31. S
4. S	11. T	18. S	25. S	32. S
5. S	12. S	19. S	26. S	33. S
6. S	13. T	20. S	27. S	34. S
7. S	14. T	21. T	28. T	35. T/S

**Going in
Circles**

Paragraph 1.

    Transitions used: Below, upward, along, middle, out into the crater, over the sides, down the outer wall, onto the land.

Paragraph 2.

    Transitions used: At the top, Below, The top surface, Below the rim, out, down, inward.

**Your Own
Space**

    A ten-speed begins at the handlebars, which are curved down and toward the rider so the person must lean low over the bike. From the middle of the handle bars a one-inch shaft runs down into a steering column, which connects the front forks and wheel to the rest of the bike. From the center of the steering column a steel tube runs parallel to the ground and breaks into a pair of forks just behind the seat, which is perched at the very top of this structure. At the bottom of this framework hang the pedals and main sprockets that drive the bike.

    The nurse's office was to the right of the main doors as we came into the hospital lobby. It was a small room, painted yellow and decorated with pictures of his family and fishing pals. Just to the right of the light switch hung a huge stuffed fish with a mouth big enough to swallow a small canoe. Above the fish hung a long bamboo fishing pole like you see in the old pictures of Huck Finn and Tom Sawyer. Opposite the doorway was a wall of bottles, all colors and sizes, and at the exact center of the bottles sat a two-foot jar with a giant eel floating in it. I was glad for all the interesting stuff because it took my mind off the tetanus shot.

**Time-Space
Report**

    Though Mrs. Claus thinks Santa is a handsome fellow, most people would probably disagree. His face is round like a cheese, and around his face runs a thick white beard. On top of his head sits a red wool cap trimmed in white fur, the same fur that trims his red coat. Beneath his coat lies a huge belly that is ringed by a shiny black belt wide enough to act as a girdle, and below his belt are red wool pants that end at the tops of his knee-high black boots. If he were walking in the park or along the beach, most folks would think he was rather strange.

    The legend of this unhandsome character was first based on the real Saint Nicholas, who lived in the town of Myra, Turkey, about A.D. 300. By the sixth century A.D. people saw Saint Nicholas as the patron saint of school kids. Later, in the Middle Ages, he was pictured as a furry little elf in Germany. When the 1800's rolled around, Saint

Nicholas was described by the American writer Washington Irving as a jolly fellow who smoked a pipe. Then in 1822 Clement Moore wrote "The Night Before Christmas" and made Saint Nicholas into Santa Claus, the elf with a kind heart and a beard the color of new-fallen snow.

Time and Space Together

The use of coins as money goes back many centuries. The Chinese are said to have used the first metal coins, made of bronze, around 1100 B.C.; they were made in the shapes of hoes, knives, and keys. Then about 400 years later, the Lydians began using silver to make coins, followed by the Aegeans, who used pure silver in the shape of a turtle. Later still, King Croesus used pure gold, and finally King Philip of Macedon issued the first "modern" coin using copper in about 359 B.C.

Of all the coins ever minted, one of the most interesting is the modern-day American quarter. At the center of one side sits the image of the first U.S. president, George Washington. Above his head is stamped the word "LIBERTY," and under his chin are printed the words, "In God We Trust." At the base of the image is the year when the coin was issued. On the reverse side is an eagle with wings spread. Over its head are the words "The United States of America" and below, at the eagle's feet, are the words "Quarter Dollar." No one would deny that this coin is full of interesting details.

Section 4: Summarizing

Find the "Sum Totals"

A. Your parents will be very worried.

B. You will call your parents for a ride home after play tryouts.

C. You will work for Grandma this summer.

Get to the Point

Come get me 8:00 A.M. Saturday main office. Roger.

More Summaries

The Wizard of Oz: A tornado whisks a girl to a fantasy land called Oz where she meets many odd beings including the Wizard who helps her get back home.

Treasure Island: A boy hunts for buried treasure in the company of a pirate who the boy thinks is his friend.

Rudolph the Red-Nosed Reindeer: A deer with a glowing-nose deformity saves the day when Santa needs someone to light the way on a foggy Christmas Eve.

**The Summary
Syndrome**

Paragraph 1.   Buses, trains, and aircraft pump millions of tons of pollutants into the earth's atmosphere while consuming millions of gallons of the world's oil supply.

Paragraph 2.   Other contributors to America's energy waste are cars and tools (like chain saws and lawn mowers) and recreational vehicles (like motorcycles and powerboats).

**Be a
"Summary"
Warrior**

Summary Sentence for Paragraph 1:   Earth experiences over a million earthquakes a year, but only about 20 per year cause serious changes in the earth's surface.

Summary Sentence for Paragraph 2:   Major earthquakes kill 10,000 to 15,000 people a year, and over the time of recorded history, 13 million people are known to have died from earthquakes.

Summary Sentence for Paragraph 3:   Earthquakes strike everywhere on earth and at all times; it has always been this way.

Summary Paragraph

The earth experiences over a million earthquakes a year, but only about 20 per year cause serious changes in the earth's surface. The serious quakes kill about 10,000 to 15,000 people each year, and since recorded history over 13 million people are known to have been killed by earthquakes. They occur everywhere on earth and at all times of the year; it has always been this way.

Combination II   Summary Sentence for Paragraph 1:   When the Yellowstone fire of 1988 began, the Park Service decided to let it burn, and the winds blew the fire out of control.

Summary Sentence for Paragraph 2:   Army troops and firefighters using helicopters and air tankers fought the fire for months.

Summary Sentence for Paragraph 3:   The fire destroyed homes, cabins, and animals but was eventually stopped at a cost of $3 million a day.

Summary Paragraph:

When the Yellowstone fire of 1988 began, the Park Service decided to let it burn, and the winds blew the fire out of control. Army troops and firefighters using helicopters and air tankers fought the blaze for months. The result was that it destroyed cabins, homes, and animals and was eventually stopped at a cost of $3 million a day.

Section Five: Paraphrasing

Para-
Practice II

1. Cable TV companies are putting on more educational programs in order to compete with *Channel One*, a new 12-minute program that is being played in schools nationwide. Many states don't want *Channel One* in their schools because the program includes commercials, so cable TV companies see a chance to increase their business in students' homes.

2. The best clocks and calenders made by early civilizations were designed by the Babylonians; they covered 360 days and 12 months. This was the result of 5,000 years of struggle to match numbers to the flow of time.

Para-
Practice III

HOMELESS

America has a problem with homeless children because they don't go to school very often. Up to 200,000 move from town to town each year and never get a regular, solid education, (*The New York Times,* Feb. 21, 1988). The government now spends $3 milllion to educate homeless kids each year.

TRUANCY

Kids who skip school are being helped by KIDS, an organization that supplies brand-new clothes to students who can't afford to buy them. The program is now being used in San Francisco. It was started in New York in 1985 and has given more than $3 million in new clothes to kids who would otherwise not go to school because of their poor appearance. (*The New York Times,* April 7, 1988)

Para-
Practice IV

SEQUOIAS

Being the toughest tree in the world the giant sequoia can take 20-foot snowfalls and zero-degree temperatures without being affected. Twenty-five million years ago giant sequoias were found in many different places like Texas, Japan, and France. But today they are only in California on the slopes of the Sierra Nevada. (Stewart, p. 64)

SPIDERS

Spiders have survived on earth for about 380 million years, according to scientists, because of their skills with silk; they store their eggs in silk sacs, catch their prey in silk webs, and send messages by plucking the fine silk threads of the webs of their neighbors. (*Discover,* p. 21)

Be a Transformer

Little League baseball has become an important part of life for millions of kids in the United States today. Starting in 1939 in Williamsport, Pennsylvania, Little League today has 11,000 leagues and 3 million players. According to a law signed by President Ford in 1974, girls are now allowed to participate and all players, girls or boys, must be between 8 and 12 years old and must have their parents' consent.

Transformer II

REINDEER

Reindeer are interesting creatures. They are only 3′6″ high, weigh about 300 pounds, have poor eyesight, and have horns shaped like an elk's. They provide food, clothing, and hauling power for the people of Lapland, who take great care with these animals; the Laplanders track them in herds by using radar collars and bells around the reindeer's necks.

FUTURE TRAINS

Trains are changing the way the world travels. The new ones are so fast that many people will probably travel in them rather than in airplanes. The "maglev" train, for example, is being developed in Germany at a cost of $1 billion. It will travel 300 miles per hour by means of magnets that actually "lift" the train off the tracks, and will look something like a jetliner without wings.

Transformer III

Everybody by now has heard about the most successful fast-food restaurant in the world: McDonald's. Mr. Ray Kroc started the first McDonald's restaurant in Des Plaines, Illinois, in 1955 after he'd bought the name and the idea from the McDonald brothers in San Bernardino, California. Soon Mr. Kroc's restaurants were showing up everywhere through the idea of a "franchise." Then, to keep the fast, efficient quality to his business, he created the Hamburger University where workers are trained. Today his restaurants are known worldwide for good food and quick service.

Transformer
IV

The Peace Corps is not a new idea today, but it was in 1960. President Kennedy decided the United States needed a way to help other countries who were struggling to survive, so he suggested the idea to Congress. By 1961 Congress had set up the Peace Corps, but then the Corps declined and by 1968 it was in trouble. In 1981 President Reagan brought the Peace Corps back to strength. Since it began in the early 1960's, the Peace Corps has served 99 countries with over 122,000 volunteers.

But critics said the Peace Corps was originally created to make President Kennedy look good. Furthermore, some claimed that Peace Corps workers were not very skilled and were of little help once they got to other countries. In fact, there was a name for the Peace Corps that wasn't very pleasant: Kennedy's Kiddie Korps. But today the Peace Corps is strong and moving again in 68 countries around the world. And at home in the United States, the Peace Corps is adopting school classrooms to which workers send letters and pictures to students to tell them what their work is like.

Section Six: Using Quotes

Which Quotes
to Use?   1a. V   2a. V   3a. I   4a. V   5a. V
             1b. I   2b. I   3b. V   4b. I   5b. I

Expert Opinion 1a,   2a,   3a,

Choose the
Quotes   Most effective quotes are:
                  1. b, c
                  2. b, c, d

Quotes in
Your Notes   **QUOTE:**

"Jobs now exist at all colleges, many high schools, and even some junior and middle schools. . . . I recommend high schoolers take a strong science program, particularly biology and chemistry, and also develop good math skills."

Source: "Ronnie Barnes: Athletic Trainer of Champions," *Career World,* Nov. '89, p. 8

*Making
Quotes*

QUOTE:

"We were always considered a sleeping giant, and then, in 1982, we discovered snowmaking, invested $8 million in a plant and machinery, and sat back to count the returns." M. Filion, co-owner of Mont Sainte-Anne ski resort.

Source: Needham, Dick, "Annie Gets Her Guns," *Ski*, Feb. 1989, p. 76

Quote: "We know a lot more than we did 15 years ago, but there are major gaps in our knowledge. We don't really know why tornadoes occur." Howard Bluestein, meteorologist.

Source: Roman, Mark, "Tornado Tracker," *Discover,* June 1989, p. 51

*Using
Quotes*

QUOTE REWRITE:

Emanuel Rubin, pathologist at Jefferson Medical College in Philadelphia, says, "The more alcohol consumed in a lifetime, the less strength of the heart and the less strength of the muscles."

*Using More
Quotes*

QUOTE REWRITE:

Dr. Peter Holcomb, scientist at U.W. Labs in Paris, France, says, "No scientist has complete and accurate data on how much pollution it will take to make life on this planet impossible."

QUOTE REWRITE:

Dr. Marilyn Repshire, head of the child development program at Burns Clinical University, Agnes, Australia, says, "Kids today are emotionally stronger than kids were 40 years ago because they must make much tougher decisions under a variety of stressful situations."

*Credit for
Quotes I*

Pit Bulldogs   "These dogs have the jaw strength of a lion. They are time bombs, and their owners don't know what they have until it's too late." (Reynolds, p. 46)

Tanning Salons   "There's no way for a consumer to know how much ultraviolet radiation is coming out of the tanning unit." (Slom, p. 94)

Credit for
Quotes II   *Microwave Ovens*   "The microwave is what I call an attractive hazard."
                          (Shapiro, p. 56)

             The Sun   "If a good case could be made for the sun's
                          influence on weather, then that fact alone would be
                          more important than anything else studied in solar-
                          terrestrial physics." (Bartusiak, p. 45)

Section 7: Crediting Information

Credit the
Facts   (Brody, p. 63)

Crediting I   (Kiester, p. 49)
             (Kaufman, p. 60)

Crediting II   (Carlson, p. 28)
             (Hanauer, p. 42)
             (Leslie, p. 12)

To Credit or
Not to Credit   1. G   5. C

                2. C   6. C

                3. G   7. G

                4. G   8. G

What Gets
Credit?   1. G   8. C

          2. G   9. G

          3. C   10. G

          4. C   11. C

          5. G   12. G

          6. G   13. G

          7. G   14. C

Section 8: Writing Conclusions

Meet the
General   If you want proof that potato chips are popular, attend any picnic in
          any park; on most tables will sit a bag of chips with most of the chips
          missing.

**Find the
G.O.S.**

1. No matter how busy . . . as long as there are newspapers.

2. No one doubts that what we think . . . business and education.

3. Little did they know . . . a home for "pilgrims."

4. It is no wonder . . . Americans who ever lived.

**Generally
Speaking**

G.O.S.:

1, 3, 6, 7, 8, 9, 10, 11, 14, 15, 16, 17, 18, 20

**Opinion,
Please**

1. Cliff divers thrill audiences every time they leap out over the rocks.

2. Television news has become something millions of people rely on every day.

3. Dr. Martin Luther King left a legacy of freedom not only for the United States but also for the world.

4. Throwing trash onto streets, roads, and public trails shows little respect for the land and the people on it.

Your Turn

1. Swimming is not only healthy and inexpensive, especially if you live near a public beach, but also essential to anyone who plans to fish, boat, or water-ski. It could be the difference between dying in a water accident or living to tell about it.

2. People came west for a lot of reasons—to get free land, to be free from slave masters, or to gain a fortune by selling and trading. Some of these people failed, but none of them could say they didn't experience some thrill of western adventure along the way.

In Conclusion

A woman of great genius, Marie Curie made her mark in the world of science by being intelligent, brave, and above all, determined. The Nobel Prize was the world's way of saying thanks, but the true mark of Curie's commitment to science is that she would have gone on with her work in radioactive substances regardless of what anyone thought or whether the world ever took notice.

When the Soviets sent up *Sputnik* in 1957, the race to explore space was on. Though many today see the "race" as something that should be done as a team effort, few will ever forget the day when that first satellite burst through our atmosphere and ignited our imaginations. It showed what people could do with scientific information. And it proved that humans will freely spend themselves and their resources on the quest to know what's out there.

Report Topics

General Report Topics

1. acid rain
2. advice columns
3. aerobic workouts
4. AIDS
5. airline safety
6. allergies
7. American flag
8. American folklore
9. anorexia
10. ant farms
11. antique cars
12. antitheft devices
13. aquariums
14. arc welding
15. Arctic
16. arm wrestling
17. assault weapons
18. assembly-line robots
19. Australian Outback
20. autistic children
21. Aztecs
22. baby toys
23. bagpipes
24. baking
25. ballet dancing
26. balloons
27. barnacles
28. baseball cards
29. Bastille Day
30. Battle of Vicksburg
31. Bay of Pigs invasion
32. BB guns
33. beauty contests
34. beef jerky
35. Berlin Wall
36. bicycle racing
37. Big Ben (the clock)
38. Bikini Islands
39. bingo
40. black powder guns
41. blue jeans
42. blue laws
43. blue light specials
44. body building
45. body language
46. bone cancer
47. boxing
48. braces (teeth)
49. brain
50. brain surgery
51. brain tumors
52. breakfast food
53. breaking horses
54. briefcases
55. broadcasting
56. bull riding
57. butterflies
58. cactus
59. caffeine
60. calendars
61. calligraphy
62. candlemaking
63. canker sores
64. cannibals
65. canoe racing
66. capitalism
67. Capone, Al
68. CB radios
69. cheetahs
70. Cherokee Indians
71. chewing gum
72. chewing tobacco
73. Cheyenne Indians
74. child abuse
75. children's museums
76. Christmas
77. cigarettes
78. classical music
79. classified ads
80. cliff diving
81. cocaine
82. cockroaches
83. combination locks
84. comets
85. comic books
86. comic strips
87. communism
88. computers
89. condors
90. Constitution
91. contact lenses
92. continental drift
93. corrective shoes
94. counterfeit money
95. cowboy boots
96. coyotes
97. CPR (cardiopulmonary resuscitation)
98. crack cocaine
99. credit cards
100. crossbows
101. Crusades
102. cures for a cold
103. cystic fibrosis
104. Death Valley
105. diamonds

106. diaries
107. disk jockeys
108. Disney, Walt
109. dog grooming
110. Down's syndrome
111. dragons
112. dreams
113. drivers' tests
114. drug traffic
115. dry ice
116. duck soup
117. earphones
118. earthquakes
119. Easter eggs
120. echoes
121. ecology
122. Edison, Thomas
123. Egyptian pyramids
124. electoral college
125. electric chair
126. electric guitars
127. electric typewriters
128. electrocution
129. elevator shoes
130. euthansia
131. eye shadow
132. fairy tales
133. faith healing
134. fake jewelry
135. false teeth
136. family farms
137. fast food
138. FAX machines
139. figure skating
140. fire ants
141. fish farming
142. fleas
143. Fort Knox
144. Fort Laramie
145. foster homes
146. fourth dimension
147. *Foxfire*
148. *Frankenstein*
149. freckles
150. French fashions
151. Freud, Sigmund
152. Fuller, Buckminster
153. furniture building
154. G-forces
155. gag gifts
156. generators
157. geniuses
158. getting rich
159. giant pumpkins
160. giant squid
161. glass-making
162. gliders
163. gold
164. goldfish
165. Grand Canyon
166. grand pianos
167. hair curlers
168. hairstyles
169. Halley's Comet
170. health spas
171. heart monitors
172. helicopters
173. hemophilia
174. herbal medicine
175. *Hindenburg*
176. hitchhiking
177. holograms
178. Hoover Dam
179. horror movies
180. housecleaning
181. Hula-Hoop
182. hurricanes
183. ice cream
184. icebergs
185. idiot savants
186. infrared light
187. ink
188. ironman triathlon
189. Jack the Ripper
190. Japanese cars
191. jazz
192. jungle frogs
193. junk bonds
194. kangaroo rats
195. karate
196. kayaking
197. kidney transplants
198. knee surgery
199. Koran
200. kryptonite
201. Ku Klux Klan
202. ladybugs
203. laser discs
204. laser printers
205. lawn mowing
206. lawn ornaments
207. leather jackets
208. leftovers
209. Liberty Bell
210. listening devices
211. lobsters
212. locusts
213. log cabins
214. LSD
215. maggots
216. mail-order catalogs
217. makeup
218. meat-eating plants
219. Medusa
220. memory
221. memory loss
222. mercenaries
223. metal detectors
224. meteorites
225. Mickey Mouse

226. micro robots
227. milk testers
228. Milky Way
229. millionaires
230. miniature paintings
231. mink farms
232. model planes
233. monks in America
234. moon (the)
235. moon phases
236. Morse code
237. motorcycle racing
238. Mount St. Helens
239. mountain climbing
240. mouse traps
241. music boxes
242. music video
243. national lottery
244. neon signs
245. Niagara Falls
246. nicotine
247. night school
248. nightmares
249. nuclear bombs
250. oil painting
251. okra
252. omelets
253. open-heart surgery
254. orange juice
255. organ grinders
256. orphans
257. otters
258. owls
259. palomino horses
260. pandas
261. pantomime
262. panty hose
263. paper routes
264. parachuting
265. park rangers
266. parrots

267. peaches
268. Pearl Harbor
269. pearls
270. penguins
271. penny stocks
272. pentathlon
273. perfume
274. pesticides
275. pet collars
276. pet food
277. pet motels
278. pit bulldogs
279. pizza making
280. plastic surgery
281. Pluto
282. poaching
283. poisonous plants
284. poisons
285. police bicycles
286. polluted oceans
287. porpoises
288. potatoes
289. pottery
290. puffer fish
291. puppetry
292. puzzles
293. Quakers
294. quarter horses
295. racehorses
296. radio waves
297. rain forests
298. rainbows
299. raising rabbits
300. rattlesnakes
301. refrigerators
302. remote control
303. rescue teams
304. Richter scale
305. rock stars
306. rodeo clowns
307. running shoes

308. rural poverty
309. saber-toothed tigers
310. Sacajawea
311. salamanders
312. sassafras
313. scuba diving
314. seaweed
315. *Sesame Street*
316. sharks
317. sheep dogs
318. shin splints
319. shoplifting
320. sketching
321. skin cancer
322. skyscrapers
323. snorkeling
324. Snow White
325. soybeans
326. Space Needle
327. space stations
328. Special Olympics
329. square dancing
330. stamp collecting
331. stamps
332. standup comedians
333. static electricity
334. steroids
335. stilts
336. stock market
337. Stonehenge
338. street people
339. stunt people
340. subways
341. sugar
342. summer camps
343. sunglasses
344. Super Bowl
345. surgical zippers
346. suspenders
347. table tennis
348. tacos

349. Tasmanian devils
350. tattoos
351. taxes
352. teen alcoholism
353. teen movies
354. teenage fashion models
355. teenage prisons
356. tennis elbow
357. tennis shoes
358. termites
359. terrorists
360. test-tube babies
361. Thanksgiving
362. Three Musketeers
363. tidal waves
364. tinsel
365. toxic wastes
366. train robbers
367. trash recycling
368. treason
369. trombones
370. tropical rain forests
371. *U.S.S. Constitution*
372. UFOs
373. UNICEF
374. unicorns
375. Venus
376. video recorders
377. violence on TV
378. volcanoes
379. voodoo
380. wallabies
381. wanted posters
382. warships
383. warts
384. water moccasins
     (snakes)
385. wax museums
386. weightlessness
387. welfare
388. white water rafting
389. windmills
390. Wonder, Stevie
391. woodcarving
392. Wright brothers
393. writing pens
394. X rays
395. yachts
396. yearbooks
397. yo-yo tricks
398. yogurt
399. Zeus
400. zodiac signs

Social Studies Report Topics

401. Adams, Abigail
402. Adams, Samuel
403. Alamo
404. Alaska, purchase of
405. Battle of Bull Run
406. Boone, Daniel
407. CIA
408. Cold War
409. Columbus, Christopher
410. cotton gin, changes
     brought by
411. depth charges
412. Earhart, Amelia
413. French and Indian War
414. Gettysburg Address
415. Gorbachev, Mikhail
416. Grant, Ulysses S.
417. guerrilla warfare
418. Hitler, Adolf
419. Jamestown, Virginia
420. Jefferson, Thomas
421. Kennedy, John F.
422. Kent State
423. King, Coretta
424. Lee, Robert E.
425. life in the original
     13 Colonies
426. Lincoln, Abraham
427. Louisiana Purchase
428. Manhattan Project
429. Mann, Horace
430. McAuliffe, Christa
431. Missouri Compromise
432. NATO
433. O'Connor, Sandra Day
434. Panama Canal
435. Patton, General
436. Pilgrims
437. Pitman, Miss Jane
438. Ride, Sally
439. St. Lawrence River
440. secession of
     Southern states
441. socialism
442. Thatcher, Margaret
443. trench warfare in
     World War I
444. Underground Railroad
445. Valley Forge
446. Vespucci, Amerigo
447. Vietnam War
448. Warsaw Pact
449. Washington, George
450. Whitney, Eli

Science Report Topics

451. acidic soil
452. aspirin, effects of
453. atom, makeup of
454. cell parts
455. centripetal force
456. clouds, types of
457. crystals
458. DNA
459. eclipses
460. erosion
461. friction
462. genes
463. geysers
464. gravity
465. gymnosperms
466. high pressure (weather)
467. hormone production
468. human circulation
469. human zygote, early development of
470. hurricanes, causes of
471. Ice Age
472. igneous rock
473. levers
474. light waves
475. low pressure (weather)
476. Mars
477. Mendel, Gregor
478. metamorphic rock
479. microscope's invention
480. neurons
481. Newton, Isaac
482. Newton's laws
483. nuclear energy dangers
484. nuclear reactors
485. ocean floor makeup
486. Old Faithful
487. periodic table
488. pituitary gland
489. placental mammals
490. Plato's science
491. pulleys
492. radiation
493. revolution of earth
494. RNA
495. rotation of earth
496. San Andreas Fault
497. sedimentary rock
498. sound waves
499. ultraviolet radiation
500. warm fronts

CHAPTER 1:

FINDING A TOPIC

What's a Report?

When you were born, the nurse filled out a report on you:

NAME ....

LENGTH ....

WEIGHT ....

DATE OF BIRTH ....

TIME OF BIRTH ....

MOTHER'S NAME ....

FATHER'S NAME ....

NAME OF HOSPITAL ....

NAME OF ATTENDING PHYSICIAN .....

Then you signed this report with your foot!

Reports are still a big part of your life.

Example: Can you name the little piece of paper that follows you home from school once in a while and tells how you've been doing?

It's called a **report** card.

Depending upon what's in the report, you can live in peace and prosperity or spend the rest of your life in your room studying science workbooks.

The **report** card tells:

WHO .... you

WHAT .... your grades were excellent

WHEN .... this marking period

WHERE .... at school, of course

WHY .... because you learned your lessons

Name _____ Date _____

A Report Is . . .

"Jodie's python just ate everything in the house, including Jodie!"

"Kim and Tim kissed all through the movie."

"Only very short people were allowed in the aquarium."

Each of these sentences is a report. Someone is giving factual information and someone else is receiving that information. Nobody's opinion is given, just the facts.

That's a report.

But these are very poor reports.

WHO   set up the date with Kim and Tim?

WHEN   were they secretly introduced?

WHERE   was Tim's girlfriend during all this kissing?

WHY   were they together in the first place?

WHAT   are their true feelings for each other?

WHAT   is Kim's boyfriend going to do now?

A report tells facts.

A report uses the 5 *W*'s to include all important information.

A report does not offer an opinion—just facts.

Why Write It?

Good question. Why write reports at all? Why spend time gathering information? Why put all that work into getting words on paper?

There are a hundred good reasons to write reports.

Here's #1: Your family wants to go on a trip this spring. Your parents say, "All right. But where will we go? What sights should we see? What will all this cost? What's the best route to take? Should we fly or drive or take a bus or train or boat?" It's report time. You gather the information, comparing all the different costs and attractions and means of travel, and write it up and present it to your family. They decide on Disneyland by car. Your "reporting" skills have saved the day.

Here's #2: After deciding on Disneyland, another question arises: What's the best way to raise the extra money for the trip: cut the food budget, take on extra jobs, sell some stuff, rent out the basement? Your report on trip possibilities impressed everybody, so you are elected to gather information on the best ways to raise extra money in a household. The sooner you get it done, the sooner everybody gets to meet Mickey!

Name _____ Date _____

Here's Why

Any time you collect information and organize it in order to make a decision or to influence someone else's decision, you are using "report" skills. Learning how to write a good report would help you tremendously in the following situations.

SHOPPING .... You want to buy a car, not a lemon, so you gather information on 500 different models: their features and prices and road tests and resale values, and then make a good decision.

WORK .... Your boss says: "We need someone to travel to Europe to *report* on how our blue jeans are selling: Who's buying them? Are ours more stylish than the competition's? Is there room for expansion—more stores or catalogs or warehouse outlets?"

NOW you'll be glad you can write a great report.

LEISURE .... A fish canning company wants to set up a new factory just down the beach from your vacation cabin. You think the whole idea stinks. It's time to write a convincing letter to the town council and the mayor telling them all the *facts* about how the fish factory will ruin the beach, the water, and the tourism trade if it is built so close to all the cottages, restaurants, and boat rental places.

EDUCATION ...... You are the president of the board of education of Swap City School District #1. Your present superintendent is retiring, and you have been given the job of interviewing five candidates and *reporting* back to the board on their qualifications for the position.

MOVING .... You have your pick of three famous hotels to manage: one in New Orleans, one in New York, and one in Paris. But which community would be best for you and your family in terms of schools, medical care, social/cultural life, churches, and recreation? You had better gather some accurate information before deciding. Your future depends on it.

Show and Tell

Reports show and tell: They show how to do something or how something works; or they tell about a person, place, or thing, like the Loch Ness Monster.

To do this, reports tell: WHO

                                 WHAT

                                 WHERE

                                 WHEN

                                 WHY (or HOW)

Below is a short report. Read it and scout out the 5 *W*'s: WHO, WHAT, WHERE, WHEN, WHY. List the *W*'s on the lines provided.

In New England every spring, hundreds of teens make pancake syrup, not in the laboratory, but in the woods. They drill a hole 3″ deep and ⅜″ in diameter into sugar maple trees, tap a metal spout into each hole, and hang a bucket on each spout. Soon, clear drops of sugar water, called "sap," come dripping into the pail. When 40 to 45 gallons of sap are collected, the whole batch is boiled down to one gallon of golden maple syrup. At $30 to $40 per gallon, it can be a good way to keep the savings account healthy.

WHO _____

WHAT _____

_____

WHERE _____

WHEN _____

WHY _____

Name _____ Date _____

First Report

Remember when you were a kid and you stood up in front of the class and told how you ate some stuff that you thought was spinach but it wasn't, and afterwards you acted strange in front of the minister at dinner, and then you realized you ate 20 leaves of catnip?

That was your first report.

You were telling the class some information. They were learning. They were also laughing, but we won't talk about that.

Reports *show* and *tell*. And they use facts to do it.

Below is a short report about making water on the moon. On the lines provided, write the information that corresponds to the 5 W's.

Scientists Roberta Bustin and Everett Gibson have recently discovered that moon rocks contain large amounts of hydrogen; about a gallon for every 8 pounds of rock. All that is required is to heat the rock to 1,650 degrees, and the hydrogen will combine with oxygen and form water—lots of it! So life on a moon base might be easier and happen sooner than we think.

WHO _____

WHAT _____

_____

WHEN _____

WHERE _____

WHY _____

This Is News!

Reports are news—pieces of information put together to inform and teach people about their world.

Below are five pieces of information. Use them to write a super-brief report that includes all five *W*'s:

WHO . . . . . Mikhail Gorbachev

WHAT . . . . Visited the United States

WHEN . . . . December 7, 1988

WHERE . . . New York City; the United Nations Building

WHY . . . . . To tell the world that the Soviet Union would be withdrawing 500,000 troops from bases around the globe

REWRITE

_____

_____

_____

_____

_____

_____

_____

_____

_____

_____

_____

Name _____   Date _____

Do It Again!

Put the information listed below into a short report, maybe one or two sentences. Try to sound like an authority, like Dan Rather telling the evening news.

WHO . . . . . teenagers

WHERE . . . in schools across the United States

WHEN . . . . every day

WHAT . . . . on the average 4,000 drop out of school; a total of 700,000 per year

WHY . . . . . • gifted students are bored

                   • serious behavior problems

                   • poor academic skills

                   • poor self-image

                   • belief that they don't need school

SHORT REPORT

_____

_____

_____

_____

_____

_____

_____

_____

_____

_____

_____

_____

Name _____   Date _____

And Once More

Write the information listed below into a short, interesting report. Use two or three sentences. Make the report sound as though it is coming from an expert . . . YOU!

WHO . . . .   Peter Diamond

WHEN . . .   recently

WHERE . .   Peter is from Tunkhannock, Pennsylvania

WHAT . . .   He has designed a removable passenger compartment for commercial jets that will eject the entire planeload of passengers at one time and land them safely by parachute. The plane would then land in a field, desert, or ocean using autopilot controls.

WHY . . . .   Hundreds of people die every year during landings when the plane has had an engine failure or landing-gear problem.

SHORT REPORT

_____

_____

_____

_____

_____

_____

_____

_____

_____

_____

_____

_____

Opinion or Fact?

Reports are based on facts, not opinions, and to write a good report you must be able to decide what is a fact and what is not.

Facts are things that are true, that can't be changed. Ever.

Opinions are personal beliefs that are open to argument and that can't be proven to everyone's satisfaction.

For example: You could say,   "President Reagan was the only American president to have been a movie actor."

This is a fact. No one would argue with it. It's absolutely true.

Or you could say,   "President Reagan was the greatest president America has ever had."

This statement is not absolutely true for all people everywhere. It is *not* a fact. It is someone's opinion, which may differ from another person's idea of who the greatest American president really was (Abraham Lincoln, or George Washington, for example).

HINT: You can spot opinions by watching for the words "I think" or "I believe."

Also, words like "best," "worst," and "greatest" tell you that someone is ranking something on a mental scale from best to worst. They are not stating facts when they use these kinds of words.

And some people say we "should" do this, or "shouldn't" do that. They are stating their opinions. They are not stating facts that everyone would agree on as being true.

Name _____ Date _____

Fact Finding

Below is a list of facts and opinions.

Mark the opinions with an **O** and mark the facts with an *F*.

Examples: _F_ The earth revolves around the sun.

             _O_ I believe there is human life on other planets.

Remember: When people ask or write opinions they often use:

"should"	"shouldn't"
"greatest"	"best"
"finest"	"worst"
"I think"	"I believe"

1. _____ I think China is the most beautiful country in the world.

2. _____ The people of China eat mostly rice.

3. _____ Rice is the best food you can eat.

4. _____ If Americans want to stay healthy, they should eat a lot of rice.

5. _____ The Great Wall of China is the most beautiful human-made structure in the world.

6. _____ The Great Wall of is made of millions of stones.

7. _____ The poem "Mending Wall" is by Robert Frost.

8. _____ The poem says, "Good fences make good neighbors."

9. _____ I think Robert Frost would have loved the Great Wall of China.

How to Write Reports

Fact Practice

Reports are made of facts. And to write a good report, you need to know how to recognize facts when you see them.

For example, this statement is a fact: "Thanksgiving is always in November." (You can look it up on a calendar.)

But this statement is not a fact: "Thanksgiving is the best holiday of the year." (This is an opinion of someone who loves Thanksgiving.)

Identify the facts below by placing an **F** next to them. Mark the opinions with an **O**.

Examples: __F__ Christmas comes once a year.

__O__ Santa Claus lives; I know he does!

1. _____ Bald eagles aren't really bald.

2. _____ Nothing is more beautiful than a bald eagle.

3. _____ The bald eagle has a very large wingspan.

4. _____ The number of bald eagles living in North America has declined in the past 50 years.

5. _____ Yellowstone National Park is one place eagles live.

6. _____ The United States should have chosen the turkey as its national bird instead of the eagle.

7. _____ I think it would be disgusting to eat one's national bird for a holiday meal.

8. _____ It is illegal to shoot a bald eagle in the United States.

9. _____ All eagles should be captured and shipped to the wilderness of northern Canada.

10. _____ The eagle is the symbol of the United States Postal Service.

Subject Search

To write a good, factual report you need a subject. To find a subject you can do the following:

- Sit in a bare room till a vision comes to you.
- Open an encyclopedia and dive-bomb the page with your finger.
- Draw a topic out of a hat.
- Ask your doctor.

Another way to find a subject is to ask questions:

- What do Russians eat for dessert?
- Where do snakes go in winter?
- What's it like to live in an orphanage?
- How is the lead put into a pencil?
- What is human hair made of?
- Can you make a lot of money selling Christmas cards?
- Do armadillos mate for life?
- How do dogs get to star in movies?
- Can a warm mayonnaise-and-bologna sandwich kill you?
- Do monkeys sing?
- How do you become a professional spy?
- Can cranberries cure cancer?
- How many runaways ever get back home?
- How do Eskimos survive above the Arctic Circle?
- How do babies learn to talk?
- Can cows eat fish?
- What did the pioneers eat for snacks?
- How does a TV antenna work?
- Why aren't there trees on the Great Plains?
- How much does a blue whale eat?
- What was the average lifespan of a brontosaurus?
- Can we stop people from aging?
- Are humans really the smartest creatures?
- What does it take to become a model?
- Why are vegetables good for you?
- What exactly are hiccups?

More Subject Questions

- Do pineapples grow on trees?
- Who writes the dictionary?
- What is a clipping penalty?
- Why do some people parachute out of airplanes?
- Why is chocolate so popular?
- Which is heavier, fat or muscle tissue?
- Why do batteries go dead?
- Why are chalkboards green?
- How do cows make milk?
- Why can't people fly like birds?
- How much does the moon weigh?
- How long does it take to digest a pizza?
- Can animals understand TV?
- How many Americans live in the streets?
- How far can a sloth go in two hours?
- What is a sloth?
- Do cats have dreams?
- Do clowns ever get sick of being clowns?
- Can pigs walk on their hind legs?
- How much land is burned every year in the United States?
- Will game shows ever be banned from TV?

- How much does a radio commercial cost?
- Can you get a scholarship to cartoon college?
- Will humans ever become extinct?
- Who invented Tupperware parties?
- Can elephants swim?
- Why do humans get hungry?
- Why are laptop computers so popular?
- Who invented volleyball, and why?
- What is the favorite sport in India?
- Is it legal for kids to divorce their parents?
- Can you get fat from eating carrots?
- How do blind kids get through high school?
- Who invented blue jeans?
- Could just anybody learn to play the cello?
- Why don't opera stars sing in English?
- Does rock music ruin your hearing?
- How dangerous is skateboarding?
- Can the president of the United States get fired?

Questions Are the Answer

Questions can start the circuits of your brain humming—get the old computer fired up!

Questions like those on the previous pages don't give you a decent report in themselves, but they do get you looking into things, investigating subjects like volleyball, elephants, modeling, snakes, babies, and Russian culture.

Example: Take the question "Do armadillos mate for life?"

You could look this up and write "NO!" and your report would be over. But if you thought about these little creatures, you could invent a whole bunch of questions that could result in an interesting and worthwhile report . . .

Questions like: . . . Are armadillos poisonous?

. . . Will they attack if pushed too far?

. . . How do armadillos communicate?

. . . Are they reptiles or mammals?

. . . What do they eat?

. . . Are armadillos becoming extinct?

. . . What happens if one bites you?

. . . Could you raise armadillos for fun and profit?

. . . Can they be tamed?

Name _____ Date _____

You Try It!

Write five questions like those on the previous pages whose answers can be found in books or journals or encyclopedias or magazines. You may ask unusual questions, but they can't be too weird. They must be researchable on this planet, now, today, in an ordinary library. (Numbers 6, 7, and 8 are for those who dare to go where no one has gone before.)

1. _____

_____

2. _____

_____

3. _____

_____

4. _____

_____

5. _____

_____

*6. _____

_____

*7. _____

_____

*8. _____

_____

Get Curious

Below are two questions borrowed from the previous pages. Write five more questions that further investigate each subject.

1. Do clowns ever get tired of being clowns?

   a. _____

   _____

   b. _____

   _____

   c. _____

   _____

   d. _____

   _____

   e. _____

   _____

2. Which is heavier, fat or muscle tissue?

   a. _____

   _____

   b. _____

   _____

   c. _____

   _____

   d. _____

   _____

   e. _____

   _____

Stay Curious

Science has proven that the more times you do a thing, the better you get at it. So . . . write five more questions about the subjects listed below.

1. What does it take to become a fashion model?

   a. _____
   _____

   b. _____
   _____

   c. _____
   _____

   d. _____
   _____

   e. _____
   _____

2. Is it really possible to travel into the future?

   a. _____
   _____

   b. _____
   _____

   c. _____
   _____

   d. _____
   _____

   e. _____
   _____

Name _____   Date _____

Keep Asking

Think up four questions for each of the general subjects listed below. And remember, reports tell: WHO

WHAT

WHERE

WHEN

WHY (or HOW)

Ask questions using these five *W*'s as beginning words in the questions.

Example: EARTHQUAKES . . . *Who*   reports earthquakes?

           What   can be done to prevent earthquakes?

           Where   do most earthquakes occur?

           When   do earthquakes usually occur?

           Why   are earthquakes so dangerous?

HOMELESS PEOPLE

1. Who _____

2. What _____

3. Where _____

4. When _____

5. Why _____

CASTLES

1. Who _____

2. What _____

3. Where _____

4. When _____

5. Why _____

More Questions

Use any four of the five *W*'s to ask questions about the subjects listed below. Each question will lead to an answer, which might raise another question, which would bring another answer, which would create another . . .

STEREO SYSTEMS

1. W . . . _____

2. W . . . _____

3. W . . . _____

4. W . . . _____

UNIVERSITY LIFE

1. W . . . _____

2. W . . . _____

3. W . . . _____

4. W . . . _____

HOMEWORK

1. W . . . _____

2. W . . . _____

3. W . . . _____

4. W . . . _____

Narrowing Down

Below is a list of subjects that could bury you in information. Study them a moment:

- THE CIVIL WAR
- CATTLE
- HEALTH
- SPACE EXPLORATION
- SPORTS
- BEST-SELLING NOVELS

- POLITICS
- EDUCATION
- OVERPOPULATION
- TOURISM
- POLLUTION
- ELECTRICITY

These subjects need **topic titles**—phrases that state something more specific about the general subject.

Below are some topic titles based on a few of these general subjects. Any one of them would make a good start for a report without swamping you with general information.

1. THE CIVIL WAR: "Many teens fought side by side with adults during the Civil War."

2. CATTLE: "Hereford cattle were introduced into the United States by the British over 100 years ago."

3. HEALTH: "Every ounce of alcohol consumed kills one million brain cells."

4. SPACE EXPLORATION: "Manned space flight may be unnecessary by the year 2000."

Too Big

Writing on a broad, general topic is like digging a swimming pool with a spoon—you do a lot of work but don't get anywhere.

Your subject must be narrowed down to one statement that says something specific. This statement is called a **topic title**.

Take the subject of CARS, for example. Any library has dozens of books on cars—maybe hundreds. Could you read and take notes on all those books even if you wanted to? You'd have grandchildren by the time it was all over.

Find a specific topic within the huge subject of CARS:

- race cars
- dragsters
- recreational vehicles
- antique cars
- auto safety
- getting a driver's license
- solar-powered cars
- used car sales
- auto insurance for teens

Next, write a **topic title** that says something specific about one of these narrower topics.

Example: Let's say your older brother has a "fender-bender" in the mall parking lot. He's 17 and he pays $600 every six months for car insurance. Now, with this accident on his record, his insurance will go up to $900 per six months. Needless to say, your parents and brother are upset. This issue of high-priced auto insurance for teens is very personal to you. Your brother is involved. That means you're involved.

You could write about this topic in a report with this topic title: "Why teenagers are forced to pay very high auto insurance."

Your personal involvement would make this an interesting report both for you and your readers. And the topic title will help you focus on one aspect of the general subject of CARS.

23 *How to Write Reports*

Name _____ Date _____

Drawing the Line

The general subjects listed on the left are too huge to be any good. But the topic titles on the right narrow each subject down enough to be workable for a report.

Draw a line from each topic title to its corresponding subject. Notice how much more specific the topic titles are than the subjects and how much easier they would be to work with when writing a report.

CANNIBALS   When trapped and starving, normal people have been known to become cannibals.

MAIL-ORDER CATALOGS
                                 Political comic strips are used in most newspapers.

SHEEP
                                 Music videos are expensive to make.

PERFUME
                                 Many teens make money selling wool.

BREAKFAST CEREALS
                                 Sixty years ago, catalogs were geared toward farmers.

POISONS
                                 Cockroaches eat almost anything.

COMIC STRIPS
                                 Some people are professional perfume smellers.

ROCK STARS

COCKROACHES   Rock concerts have been held to raise money for the poor in countries around the world.

MOON
                                 Babies have a natural liking for sugar.

MUSIC VIDEOS
                                 The moon is the subject of many ancient myths and legends.

SUGAR

Too Big, Part II

Some topics are so big you'd write your arms off trying to tell about them—topics like:

- "The many uses of oxygen"
- "Three thousand kinds of flowers and how they grow"
- "How children become adults"
- "How some adults become children"

Look over the groups of topics listed below. Decide which topic in each group is too big to cover in a two-page report and circle the culprit. Don't make the circle as big as the topic or you'll be writing on the walls!

Group 1: The mammals of Canada

The life and times of the box turtle

How baby-sitters learn their trade

Group 2: How to save money buying makeup

Three reasons for failing grades

Computers around the world

Group 3: How to ignite fireworks safely

World hunger

How to build a boomerang

Too Big, Part III

Circle the topic that's too big for its own good.

Group 4:   Nuclear energy

The life and death of a teenage alcoholic

The effects of test stress on 13-year-olds

Group 5:   Popcorn as a health food

How to trim your poodle

Presidents of the United States

Group 6:   Explorers of the ancient world

The lost city of Pompeii

How to play water polo

Group 7:   How to grow healthy pineapples

The most famous detective agency in the Old West

Tourism in Australia

Group 8:   Piranhas and how they kill

European painters

How shorthand can save you time

Group 9:   Solar energy

How solar-powered calculators work

The effects of pimples on your self-image

Group 10:   How to become a lawyer

Injustice around the world

How the Pilgrims administered justice

Name _____ Date _____

Get Specific

To write a report you need a **subject**: CARS, for example. Then you need a specific **topic** within the subject:

- Cars of the Future
- Car Theft
- The Presidential Limousine

Then you need a **topic title** that tells what angle of the topic you're going to report on:

- "How the president's limousine is built for pretection"
- "Car theft is big business in New York City"
- "What teens will be driving in the year 2020"

The process goes from SUBJECT ———→ TOPIC ———→ TOPIC TITLE

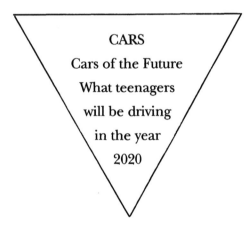

CARS
Cars of the Future
What teenagers
will be driving
in the year
2020

Note: Topic titles can lead to good thesis statements when you add an opinion to them, such as: "Teens will be driving the perfect car by the year 2020."

 How to Write Reports

Be Exact

Fill in the funnels below with specific topics and exact topic titles for the subjects listed.

Example:

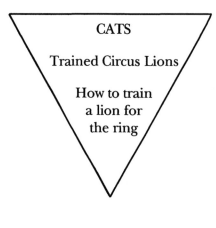

CATS

Trained Circus Lions

How to train
a lion for
the ring

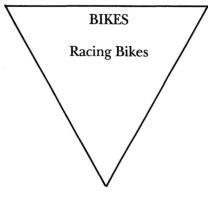

BIKES

Racing Bikes

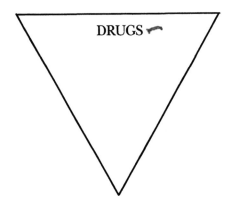

DRUGS

How to Write Reports

Monsters of the Midway

Each subject below is a monster. It's HUGE. It will devour you if you let it get out of control.

Tame these beasts by writing a **topic title** that is based on each monster subject. The topic title covers less ground than the subject and is more specific. It provides an angle on the subject.

Example: Monster Subject: SPACE EXPLORATION

Topic Title: "How Space Camp can help kids prepare for the future"

1. Monster Subject: SPORTS

   Topic Title: _____

   _____

   _____

2. Monster Subject: TRAVEL

   Topic Title: _____

   _____

   _____

3. Monster Subject: TEENAGE DRUG ADDICTS

   Topic Title: _____

   _____

   _____

4. Monster Subject: TEENAGE MAGICIANS

   Topic Title: _____

   _____

   _____

More Monsters

Write a more specific **topic title** for each of the huge monster subjects listed below. Remember: Topic titles are phrases that can be used as titles for reports, and they give direction, like a road map, to you, the writer, about what you are specifically going to say.

Example: Monster Subject: SUNSCREEN

Topic Title: Some ingredients in certain sun-blocking creams have been shown to cause cancer.

1. Monster Subject: JEWELRY

   Topic Title: _____

   _____

   _____

2. Monster Subject: UNIDENTIFIED FLYING OBJECTS

   Topic Title: _____

   _____

   _____

3. Monster Subject: VIDEO GAMES

   Topic Title: _____

   _____

   _____

4. Monster Subject: MONEY

   Topic Title: _____

   _____

   _____

Still More Monsters

Write a more specific **topic title** that would tame each of the monster subjects listed below. Before you can write an intelligent report, you need to find an angle for your subject and get more specific.

1. Monster Subject: JUNK FOOD

   Topic Title: _____

   _____

2. Monster Subject: HORROR STORIES

   Topic Title: _____

   _____

3. Monster Subject: SUNKEN TREASURE

   Topic Title: _____

   _____

4. Monster Subject: DINOSAURS

   Topic Title: _____

   _____

5. Monster Subject: LIFEGUARDS

   Topic Title: _____

   _____

6. Monster Subject: CALIFORNIA RAISINS

   Topic Title: _____

   _____

Name _____ Date _____

More Topic-Finding

Choosing a topic for a report is like choosing a topping for a sundae—the wrong one can make you sorry.

If the topic is too big, you'll end up with a bunch of general statements that sound like an outline; no details, no examples, no interesting facts.

If the topic is too small, the report won't be very good either. You won't reach many readers, and your report won't provide enough information. Reading a report with a subject that's too narrow is like being 10 minutes into a movie when the projector breaks down. You feel cheated.

Don't let your readers feel cheated; give them their money's worth.

But how do you know when a topic is too small?

Answer: When you can't find *anything* in the library on your subject, you don't know anyone who has ever heard of your subject, and your *Readers' Guide to Periodical Literature* doesn't even mention it!

Example: What if your topic title was: "How overweight reindeer fight indigestion."

You won't find one sentence about such a small, weird, silly topic in your library. And unless you can find a copy of *The Reindeer Medical Journal*, you'll be out of luck—like Rudolph on a clear night.

Remember: You must be able to research the topic in the library.

Your topic must be of interest to the general reading public. In other words, don't just write for yourself. Write to inform the world of what you have discovered.

Your report must be complete. Don't let your readers feel cheated. Avoid topics that are too small and too personal and uninteresting.

Too Small

By making your report too personal, you lose readers. A report titled "My trip over the river and through the woods to Grandma's house" would be ridiculous. Nobody cares about your trek to Grandma's except you, and maybe Grandma.

People want to learn about the world around them. They want to know how to make things, how to plan things, where to travel, where not to travel, what to eat, what not to eat, and so on.

A report on "How to make homemade ice cream" would be interesting to many people who like rich desserts.

But, a report on "How I got sick eating too much ice cream" would be of no interest to anyone except the people who had to clean up after you.

Below are five topic titles that are too small, or simply too strange, to make good reports. Look them over and think about how boring such reports would be.

- "How to pour Cheerios out of a box"
- "How the fish duck dives for fish"
- "When babies burp"
- "My summer vacation"
- "How windows steam up from cooking oatmeal"

Note: Many of these topics might make a good poem or essay. But a report is a researched piece of writing that informs the public.

Name _____ Date _____

Weed 'Em Out

Below are groups of mixed topic titles, some useful for reports and others too small and narrow.

Circle the topic title in each group that is too small for a decent report.

Example: (The day I swallowed a milk ball whole)

How to make your own malted milk shakes

The development of the milk shake in America

Group 1: How to make maple syrup

How to change your cat's litter box

The laptop computer: how it came to be

Group 2: Two ways to hold a paintbrush

How cavities form in your teeth

The hunting habits of Arctic wolves

Group 3: How to drink from a drinking fountain

The advantages of having a student council in school

How California became a state

Group 4: The main problem with juvenile detention centers

How to release a ladybug

The life and times of the teddy bear industry

Keep Weedin'

Circle the smallest, most unworkable topic in each group below.

Group 1: My trip to the dentist

The attractions at Sea World in California

The invention of the modern cash register

Group 2: How to play the autoharp while in an underwater auto

The latest allergy medicines for teenagers

How jogging affects your knees

Group 3: How some teens cope with cancer

My favorite kind of cheese

How to build your self-confidence

Group 4: A new kind of health insurance for teenagers

How to hold your fork

How the teenage magazine *Foxfire* became a huge success

Group 5: The day my pet turtle disappeared

How teens can improve their communication skills

What body language tells you about someone

Just Write I

A variety of topics are listed below in groups of three. Put a **TB** on the line next to the topics that are too big for a report; put a **TS** next to the topics that are too small and narrow for a good report; then put a **JR** next to the topics that are just right for a thorough and interesting report.

Example: **TB** Kites around the world

TS My favorite kite

JR How to build a cardboard box kite

1. _____ Child care around the world

   _____ What Mary Anderson charges to baby-sit

   _____ How to become a professional nanny

2. _____ Working parents

   _____ The role of day care centers in modern American life

   _____ How latchkey kids survive in Cheyenne, Wyoming

3. _____ Losing weight

   _____ The dangers of crash diets

   _____ How to enroll in Betty Walker's fat farm

4. _____ The sale of blue suede shoes in Cleveland in 1956

   _____ Latest blue jean fashions

   _____ Fashion around the world

5. _____ How to make a sweater from homespun yarn

   _____ Sweaters

   _____ What cashmere sweaters cost at Macy's in New York City

Just Write II

Put a **TB** next to the topics that are too big for a good report, put a **TS** next to the topics that are too small and strange, and put a **JR** next to the topics that are just right for reports.

1. _____ Worms around the world

   _____ How worms eat and digest food

   _____ How I started my worm farm in Burns, Wyoming

2. _____ How pets can affect the lives of lonely people

   _____ Pets of Australia

   _____ My dog, Rufus

3. _____ How to dip a chip

   _____ Lead poisoning

   _____ Making potato chips at home can be fun

4. _____ Fast food

   _____ The calories in a quarter-pound hamburger

   _____ How to set up and operate a hot dog stand

5. _____ What pickpockets in Ireland do on weekends

   _____ How to milk a cow

   _____ Ice cream

Topic Tips

Topics are everywhere, like suds at a dog wash.

Look.   Read.   Watch.   Listen.

You can find topics by . . .

- watching something interesting on TV.
- talking to people about their experiences.
- reading newspapers, books, magazines, maps, catalogs, diaries, calendars, encyclopedias, journals, and cereal boxes.
- looking at your own life.

You've seen things, gone places, met people, and done things that would make a dozen good reports. Use the happenings in your life to get great report topics.

Example: A big ugly bird lands on the roof of your garage. It's huge! It could eat your cat.

It has a skinny red neck with sagging pimply skin around its face. The feathers are black and oily, and it makes a deep, rattling call.

You grab your handy bird identification book and discover that it's a turkey buzzard; then you look the critter up in the encyclopedia. The facts are fascinating. The article goes on for three pages. Next, you get a book and some Audubon magazines from the library and write a report for Mr. Bindingle's science class.

Your report wins the "Perfect Scientist" award and you spend three summers in France studying French phenomena.

Your friends and experiences and interests and family can make the best report topics around if you tune in.

You are a walking report topic.

CHAPTER 2:

USING THE LIBRARY

The "Brain"

Once you've chosen your topic, narrowed it, and written your topic title, it's time to go to the "brain" of the school for information. No, it's not the kid with the laptop computer and all the answers; the "brain" of your school is the library. And to write a good report, you need to know how this "brain" functions.

The brain between your ears sorts out information and stores it in different compartments: your sense of smell is found in one part of your brain, your sense of taste in another. Your memories are catalogued in a separate area of the brain to be called out when you want them.

The library works the same way—different kinds of information are stored in different places. The trick is to find the information you need without wandering around forever looking as though you have nothing between your ears but a vague idea.

To do this you must know your library and the system it uses to sort and store information. The following exercises will help.

Also, eat your vegetables. Good research takes keen eyesight (carrots), a sharp mind (beans), and nimble fingers (brussels sprouts).

A sense of humor doesn't hurt either (cauliflower).

Inside the "Brain"

Most libraries use a system to sort and store information that was invented by a guy named Melvil Dewey.

Melvil believed in order—everything in its place. EVERYTHING. (Can you imagine what his bedroom looked like when he was a kid? Neat. Very neat.)

Melvil figured that every object, every idea, every atom of information could be listed under some general category, like *snow leopards* under CATS; or *teenagers* under HUMANS.

Then every category and subcategory and sub-subcategory (*sub* means "under"), could be given a number. For example:

FINE ARTS 700–799

under Fine Arts, RECREATION 790–799

under Recreation, TYPES OF RECREATION: Athletics 796

under Athletics, CYCLING 796.6

then different KINDS of cycling 796.60–796.69

and so on . . . and so on . . . and so on . . . !

Melvil's book on the Dewey decimal system is very, very thick. Every librarian who gets a degree in library science must study this book constantly and know what categories go under which numbers. Also, new learning is taking place every day which produces new, previously unheard-of information. This means that more decimals have to be added to Melvil's system, and no one knows for sure where the whole thing will end.

The following pages give you a brief breakdown of the general categories in the Dewey decimal system and an in-depth breakdown of one of the subcategories. You don't have to know the system inside and out in order to get a book from the library, but it is interesting to peek at how the system works. Also, a few exercises in categorizing books will help you appreciate what a librarian needs to know and do, and will give you an idea of how your school's "brain" is organized.

The Code

What does the number 796.6 stand for?

.... the number of potato chips your brother can eat in a minute?

.... the number of mosquito bites you got last summer at camp?

.... the combined weight of your Aunt Elsie and Uncle Fred?

Your librarian knows that the number 796.6 represents a book on the athletic sport of CYCLING. (If you've read the previous page, you know too!)

The librarian is simply following the Dewey decimal code for all books in the library:

General works	000–099	Science	500–599
Psychology/Philosophy ..	100–199	Applied Science	600–699
Religion/Mythology	200–299	*Fine Arts	700–799
Social Sciences	300–399	Literature	800–899
Language	400–499	Biography, History Geogaphy, Travel	900–999

The code breaks these general subjects down into smaller categories and gives each category a different number:

FINE ARTS	700–799	Painting	750–759
Landscape	710–719	Printmaking	760–769
Architecture	720–729	Photography	770–779
Sculpture	730–739	Music	780–789
Drawing	740–749	*Recreation	790–799

The Code, Part II

Then each of the subjects under RECREATION is broken down further:

RECREATION 790–799

Public
   Entertainment 791.0–791.9

Theater 792.0–792.9

Indoor Games 793.0–793.9

Indoor Games
   of Skill 794.0–794.9

Indoor Games of
   Chance 795.0–795.9

*Athletic/Outdoor
   Sports 796.0–796.9

Water Sports 797.0–797.9

Horses and Racing ... 798.0–798.9

Fishing/Hunting 799.0–799.9

Then each of these subtopics is divided into ten more subcategories:

ATHLETIC/OUTDOOR
   SPORTS 796.0–796.9

Miscellaneous Games 796.1

Active Games Requiring
   Equipment 796.2

Ball Games 796.3

Gymnastics 796.4

Outdoor Living 796.5

*Cycling 796.6

Motor Vehicle
   Sports 796.7

Combat Sports 796.8

Ice and Snow Sports 796.9

Breaking our famous number, 796.6, into finer categories would require using decimals from 796.*60*–796.*69*.

You do not need to memorize these categories, but it is fun to know how things work. And the Dewey decimal system is what most school and public libraries use to organize the thousands and thousands of books they store on their shelves.

Code Work

The ten major categories in the Dewey decimal system are listed below with a brief explanation of each. Study them closely and refer back to this page as you work the exercises in this section.

General Works 000–099   (Magazines; *Readers' Guide to Periodical Literature;* reference books like indexes, dictionaries, encyclopedias; **each reference book number is preceded by the letter *R*.)

Psychology/
Philosophy 100–199   (Books about the mind, personality, and human development.)

Religion/Mythology 200–299   (Books about gods and people's relationship with their gods.)

Social Sciences 300–399   (Books about life in society: careers, environment, justice, etc.)

Language 400–499   (Books about how people communicate—writing/speaking.)

Science 500–599   (Books on the laws/principles of life in our universe.)

Applied Science 600–699   (Books on science knowledge being put to work: medicine, fitness, plastics, lasers, etc.)

Fine Arts 700–799   (Books about how people creatively spend their time: music, art, dance, sports, painting, etc.)

Literature 800–899   (Fictional stories, books on literature, great quotations, plays, poems, famous writers.)

Biography, History
Geography, Travel 900–999   (Books about events, famous people, places, the shape and composition of the earth.)

Code Match

Write the code number of the general category in the Dewey decimal system that would include each book below.

Examples: **200** *In the Beginning,* by Virginia Haitan

900 *The History of Wyoming,* by T. A. Larsen

1. _____ *Scientists Who Changed the World,* by Lynn Poole

2. _____ *Rock Stars* (their life stories), by Steve Ditlea

3. _____ *The Black Stallion,* by Walter Farley

4. _____ *Giant Molecules,* by Herman F. Mark

5. _____ *Coping With Discrimination,* by Gabrielle Edwards

6. _____ *The Dictionary of Composers,* by Eric Gilder

7. _____ *The Civil War,* by Bruce Catton

8. _____ *Muppet Magic,* (how they work), by Patricia Frevert

9. _____ *The Music of Africa,* by Fred Warren

10. _____ *Motorcycling* (the sport), by Don Morely

11. _____ *The Mysteries of the Pharoahs* (factual information)

12. _____ *Australia* (Time–Life Books)

13. _____ *The Land and People of Mexico,* by Elsa Larralbe

14. _____ *Gods, Men, and Monsters From Greek Mythology*

15. _____ *The Magic of Words,* by Alexander Arthur

16. _____ *Protect Your Legal Rights: A Handbook for Teens*

17. _____ *First Book of Words,* by Sam Epstein

18. _____ *Psychic Stories Strange But True,* by Linda Atkinson

19. _____ *The Encyclopaedia Britannica*

20. _____ *The Teenager and the New Mysticism,* Robert Nordbey

The Unscrambling

Some of the books listed below are numbered incorrectly according to the Dewey decimal code. Cross out each incorrect number and write the correct one on the line provided. Put a **C** on the line next to each book that is numbered correctly.

Examples: ~~200~~ __400__ *The Tree of Language*

700 __C__ *Drama on the Speedway (auto racing)*

1. 005 _____ *The Puerto Ricans in America,* by Ron Larsen

2. 900 _____ *Atoms, Molecules, and Quarks,* by Melvin Berger

3. 200 _____ *Teenage Fitness,* by Bonnie Prudden

4. 800 _____ *Exploring the World of Plastics,* by G. Steele

5. 800 _____ *Battlestar Galactica*

6. 800 _____ *All About Great Medical Discoveries*

7. 400 _____ *Breaking the Language Barrier,* by Fred West

8. 300 _____ *America's Prisons: Opposing Viewpoints*

9. 200 _____ *Religions in America*

10. 100 _____ *Ten Philosophical Mistakes,* by Mortimer Adler

11. R088 _____ *The World Book Encyclopedia*

12. 700 _____ *Planning and Producing Posters,* by John Delemos

13. 700 _____ *Careers in Cartooning*

14. 500 _____ *Space Nomads: Meteorites in the Sky*

15. 500 _____ *Who Are You?* (discover you personality)

16. 100 _____ *How to Be a Successful Teenager* (taking control of your thoughts and actions)

17. 200 _____ *One God: The Ways We Worship,* by F. Fitch

18. 400 _____ *Radar Works Like This,* by Egon Larsen

Write In

Write the **name** of the general category from the Dewey decimal system that corresponds to each of the book titles listed below. (Some titles are real, some are not real.)

Examples: _____*History*_____ *The History of China*
_____*Applied Science*_____ *Robots in Your Future*

1. ——————————————— *Words, Words, Words!*

2. ——————————————— *Short Lessons in English*

3. ——————————————— *Paul Hogan: His Life and Times*

4. ——————————————— *The Idea of God*

5. ——————————————— *Solar-Powered Surfboards*

6. ——————————————— *What Do YOU Think?*

7. ——————————————— *The War of 1812*

8. ——————————————— *A Charlie Brown Christmas*

9. ——————————————— *How to Become a Cartoonist*

10. ——————————————— *The Religions of Africa*

11. ——————————————— *The History of the Fur Trade in Canada*

12. ——————————————— *Chemistry: The Science of the Mind*

13. ——————————————— *Pictures Without a Camera*

14. ——————————————— *Anne Frank: Diary of a Young Girl*

15. ——————————————— *The World Almanac*

16. ——————————————— *The Amazing Universe*

17. ——————————————— *Shortchanged by History*

18. ——————————————— *Writing: Dead or Alive*

Reference

One of the most important areas of a library is the reference section, GENERAL WORKS (0–099), because here all the reference books like dictionaries, indexes, encyclopedias, almanacs, atlases, and the *Readers' Guide to Periodical Literature* are stored. Since none of these books are allowed out of the library, a special area is set aside for readers to use the books on the spot.

Encyclopedias, for example, are reference books that have to be kept on the library shelves. They are called reference books because they *refer* to thousands of subjects from APPLES to ZEPPELINS and give background information on each. Also, at the end of most articles there is a list of additional topics that you can look up to get more information.

Example: *The World Book Encyclopedia,* Volume 16, has an article on RUBBER.

At the end of the article is the following list of topics:

Brazil	*Goodyear
Elasticity	Guayule
Faraday, Michael	Indonesia
*Firestone, Harvey	Latex
*Goodrich, Benjamin	Plastics

These topics are the key to a good report. Don't overlook them.

Hint: Include people in your reports when possible. The lives of the men who invented rubber, for instance, are fascinating—how some went without food and warm clothes in order to afford their experiments; how their children endured criticism from kids at school for having such a "crazy" father; how their wives struggled to keep the family from splitting apart like a smashed atom. (Note the starred items in the list of topics above.) If you can make people even a small part of your report, it will be much more interesting for the reader.

Command: DO NOT copy from an encyclopedia.
You are committing **plagiarism** when you steal someone else's words or opinions.

Use the encyclopedia as a springboard to get into deeper research. Books, magazines, journals, and microfiche all more fully investigate your subject.

More Reference

One reference book that will help you get into deeper research is the *Readers' Guide to Periodical Literature*. This is a book, actually a collection of books, that lists magazine articles on almost any topic imaginable:

SCHOOLS . . . DRUGS . . . KANGAROOS . . . MOVIES . . . NUTS . . . and so on.

The topics are listed alphabetically like those in an encyclopedia. Under each topic is the title of at least one magazine article, the magazine name, the author, and other important information as explained below:

Jumping

See also:

Hurdle racing

What Makes Willie Jump? [W. Banks in the triple jump] M. Kassindorf. il. por *Newsweek* 104: 26–27 Ag 6 '84

What Makes Willie Jump? .... title of article

[W. Banks in the triple jump] .... explanation of article

M. Kassindorf .... author

il .... the story is illustrated

por .... article contains a portrait

Newsweek .... name of magazine

104: 26–27 .... volume number and pages of the article

Ag 6 '84 .... date of the magazine (August 6, 1984)

Name _____ Date _____

Guide Use

Below are two subject entries found in the *Readers' Guide to Periodical Literature*.

Write the title, author's name, magazine's name, and all the other information about the entry on the lines provided, just as was done on the previous page.

Ravens

Food and feeding

The Raven's Feast. B. Heinrich. il *Natural History* pp 44–51 F '89

title _____

author _____

any illustrations? _____

magazine _____

page numbers _____

month and year of magazine _____

Hairstyling

See also:

Hairstylists

The Bob Is Back. C. Straley. il *Parents* 64:92–4 Ja '89

title _____

author _____

any illustrations? _____

magazine _____

volume number _____

page numbers _____

month and year of magazine _____

Readers' Guide Tips

The H. W. Wilson Company has put two very important pages into their *Readers' Guide to Periodical Literature* that will help you find the magazine articles you need.

FIRST, there's a code page that explains what each abbreviation in the guide stands for:

Ja = January . . .

Ap = April . . .

 v = volume . . .

 il = illustrations . . .

and so on.

  ** If you're looking up "Drug Abuse" and you find an article listed in a magazine with the letters "Ja" after the title, then you know only the January issue of that magazine carries your article.

SECOND, index pages up front list all the magazines covered by the *Readers' Guide.* If the magazine you need for your topic isn't listed in this index, chances are your library doesn't carry the magazine and you will have to go elsewhere to get your information, possibly to a university, county, or state library.

Hint: If you can't find magazines in your library that cover your topic, maybe your topic is too narrow to investigate right now. Either choose another topic, or get ready to travel, because you'll have to dig far and wide for enough information to satisfy yourself and the requirements of your report.

Note: The *Readers' Guide* is issued each month because a lot of information is being constantly published. Look for a group of green paperback books about 10″ high and 7″ wide on the reference shelves in your library. They will probably be in a section by themselves because there are so many of them that they demand their own space.

Name _____ Date _____

Quiz Time

Go to the library and study the list of abbreviations found among the first pages of any *Readers' Guide to Periodical Literature.* Then write the words that are being abbreviated on the lines below.

1. Ja _____

2. F_____

3. Mr _____

4. Ap _____

5. My _____

6. Je _____

7. Jl _____

8. Ag _____

9. S _____

10. O _____

11. N _____

12. D _____

13. il _____

14. bi-m _____

15. bibl _____

16. por _____

17. supp _____

18. introd _____

19. cont _____

20. m _____

21. v _____

22. Summ _____

23. rev _____

The Search Machine

There's been a BREAKTHROUGH!

Computerized versions of the *Readers' Guide to Periodical Literature* have invaded libraries everywhere. If yours is one of them, you are in luck, with a capital *L*!

The magazine search programs in most libraries run like this on the computer:

1. Type in the subject you are researching: DANCE, HUNTING, TELESCOPES, etc. (You don't need capital letters.)

2. A list of subheadings under the subject of DANCE, for instance, will appear on the screen. One of those headings will be "highlighted" (set off in a colored box). Press the "down" key (↓) or the "up" key (↑) to move the highlighted box to the heading you want.

3. Press the ENTER key.

4. A list of magazine articles will appear on the screen. Copy the information about any articles that look interesting. If you want to see any of the other magazine listings, press the "down" key (↓) to make them appear.

5. When you want to research a new subject, just type it in, and the computer will start a new listing of articles.

Note #1: Some search computers have a printer attached, so if you want a list of the magazines shown on the screen, just press PRINT, and you'll get a copy in a few seconds.

Note #2: If you have trouble learning the keys that operate the search program, check the box at the bottom of the screen that lists all the keys and tells what each one does. (Some computers have this printed on the plastic housing of the machine.)

If you still have trouble, *ask the librarian.*

Sources of Input

In the classic robot comedy of the 1980's, *Short Circuit*, a robot acquires the human ability to learn. As soon as the robot begins soaking up information, its electrodes go crazy and it starts yelling, "Input! Input! Input!

If you find yourself getting this excited about your report and need more input, check the following.

TOPICAL ENCYCLOPEDIAS

Many encyclopedias focus on one major topic, like: *The Color Encyclopedia of World Art, The Encyclopedia of Jazz, The Encyclopedia of Sports, Health Encyclopedia.* Check the reference section if you want any of these in-depth encyclopedias.

ALMANACS

If you need to know any world records or odd facts and figures that your magazines and encyclopedias don't seem to have, check *The World Almanac, The Information Please Almanac,* or the *Guinness Book of Records.*

BIOGRAPHIES

To get facts and background on famous people, check: *Who's Who in America, Who's Who of American Women, Who's Who in Science, Webster's Biographical Dictionary, Current Biography,* or the *Encyclopedia of World Biography.*

BOOKS IN PRINT

This is a collection of volumes that lists all the books printed in the United States today. So if you need information about WIGS, WEASELS, or WALLPAPER, you can look in the volume that lists books by subject and find several you could use. Don't worry: If your library doesn't have the books you need, it can borrow them from other libraries. Ask your librarian about "interlibrary loan." (*Books in Print* is now also on computer in some libraries.)

VERTICAL FILE

This is a file with drawers full of photos, clippings, and articles on topics of great interest to report writers like you. Check out the material just as you would a book. If the pictures and articles are extremely rare, you may have to read the material in the library and hand it back to the librarian when you are finished.

MICROFILM and MICROFICHE

To save space, many libraries store some of their information on either rolls or small sheets of film. These films are inserted into machines called "readers" which magnify the small print many times. Anyone can use these "readers," and they aren't very difficult to operate. Ask your librarian for help. You can have all the information in *The New York Times* at your fingertips, plus more if you want it.

Name _____ Date _____

The Right Source

Where would you look to find:

1. the weight of the *Queen Mary?* (the *ship,* not the person)

2. background information on rocket development?

3. a magazine article on Willie Shoemaker?

Answers: *Queen Mary* .... ALMANAC

Rockets .... ENCYCLOPEDIA

Willie Shoemaker .... *READERS' GUIDE*

In the box below are many sources of information, with a number assigned to each. Beneath the box are questions on a variety of subjects. On the line next to each question, write the number of the source(s) you would use to find the answer.

---

1. Encyclopedia
2. *Readers' Guide to Periodical Literature*
3. Vertical File
4. *Who's Who*
5. *Encyclopedia of Jazz*

6. Microfiche
7. Almanac
8. *Guinness Book of Records*
9. *Encylcopedia of Sports*
10. *Books in Print*

Note: If a subject can be researched in more than one source, put more than one number on the line.

1. _____ Who are three of the world's greatest jazz musicians?

2. _____ What is the record for staying underwater without a breathing apparatus?

3. _____ What is the population of Bangkok?

4. _____ What is it like to live along the Amazon River?

5. _____ For how long did Mickey Mantle play professional baseball?

6. _____ Where could you find a picture of the Eiffel Tower?

7. _____ What does *The New York Times* say about street gangs?

8. _____ Where can you find the title of a book that is not in the card catalog?

9. _____ Who are three famous people in American business?

10. _____ Where could you get some general information on Canada?

           How to Write Reports

Look to Books

Okay, you've looked through all the reference books you need—encyclopedias, dictionaries, the *Readers' Guide*—but you want more "input."

What do you do?

Look for a cabinet called the **card catalog** full of small drawers with letters on each drawer. Hundreds, even thousands, of cards are filed here in alphabetical order.

- If you want a book about whales, you look for a subject card with the word *WHALES* in all capital letters at the top of the card. Behind it will be filed the cards of the books the library has on whales.

- If you know the author of a book about whales, like Farley Mowat for example, you can look under "Mowat" and find the book. Author cards are filed by the author's last name.

- If you know the title of a book, like *A Whale for the Killing*, but don't know who wrote it, you can look under "Whale" and find a title card that lists the title of the book at the top. (The library doesn't alphabetize small beginning words like *the,* or *a,* or *an.*)

So to use this three-way card system, you simply need to know two things:

1. The library files three cards for every book: a subject card,
                                                   a title card,
                                                   and an author card.

2. All the subject, title, and author cards are filed together alphabetically.

File Cards

Below are three cards from the drawer marked BA–BU in the card catalog of the Burns High School library.

The first card (920) is a **subject** card because the subject of the book is printed on top of the card in all capital letters: BASKETBALL PLAYERS—U.S.

The second card (746.41) is a **title** card because the title of the book, *Basketry,* is listed at the top of the card.

The third card (978.7) is an **author** card because the author's name is printed at the top.

Note: All cards are filed in alphabetical order regardless of the type.

```
978.7        Bastian, Jean
Bas              History of Laramie County, Wyoming.
                 Curtis Media Corp., Texas. c1987.
                 461 pp.    $45.00
```

```
746.41       Basketry
Bas              Basketry by the editors of
             Consumer Guide
             Publications International c1978
             34pp.         $1.95        photos
```

```
                 BASKETBALL PLAYERS—U.S.
920          Maravich, Pete
Mar              Heir to a Dream. Thomas Nelson
                 Publishers, Nashville, TN c1987.
                 223 pp. $10.95.

                 1. Pete Maravich
                 2. Sports—U.S.—Religious aspects.

                 I. Author.      II. Title.
```

Out of Line

In the card catalog the alphabet is king!

The *G* drawer might contain the subject card GALAPAGOS ISLANDS; followed by an author card, Gallico, Paul; followed by a title card, *Gandhi*. (Some libraries have separate cabinets: one for subjects, one for titles, and one for authors.)

All of these cards must be kept in strict alphabetical order. Otherwise, finding the book *Ghandi* would take a week as you flipped through every *G* card in the library!

The subject, title, and author cards below are way out of line alphabetically. Organize them into the correct order by numbering them as follows: the first card alphabetically gets the number 1, the second card gets the number 2, the third card is number 3, and so on.

The first three are done as examples.

1. __1__ CANCER (subject)

2. _____ A Canticle for Leibowitz (title)

3. _____ Capital Punishment: Cruel and Unusual? (title)

4. __3__ The Cancer Reference Book (title)

5. _____ CANCER SURVIVAL (subject)

6. __2__ The Cancer Lady (title)

7. _____ Cane, Phillip (author)

8. _____ The Canterbury Tales (title)

9. _____ CANDLEMAKING (subject)

10. _____ Canfield, Jean H. (author)

11. _____ Cannery Row (title)

12. _____ CAPITAL PUNISHMENT (subject)

13. _____ Canton, Frank M. (author)

14. _____ Canyon of Decision (title)

Alphabet Skills

To use the **card catalog,** you need to know two things:

1. How to alphabetize words.

2. How to rank numbers from smallest to largest using decimals.

Example: Let's say you wanted a book on video games, and the drawers on the card catalog are labeled:

Va–Vi, Vi–Vo, and *Vo–Vy*

You would look in the drawer marked *Va–Vi* because your subject, VIDEO GAMES, begins with the letters *VI.* But if there are too many cards to fit in that drawer, then the second drawer, marked *Vi–Vo,* would hold the extra cards, possibly the one you want. Either way, if you stay in the first two drawers you will find something on VIDEO GAMES.

EXERCISE

Below are 10 titles of books that begin with the letter *B.* Write the number of each book on the face of the drawer that would hold its card. (When cataloging books, the beginning words *the, an,* and *a* are completely ignored.)

Example: No. 11. The Busted Cupcake

> **BR–BY**
>
> *11*

No. 1. Busy Hands Are Happy Hands

No. 2. Better Keep Hopin' It Never Rains in Jersey

No. 3. Bashful Folks Speak Out!

No. 4. Beat the "EAT" Habit

No. 5. The Bad News About Dentures

No. 6. The Boys of Black Sunday

No. 7. Bumper Crop of Bubble Gum!

No. 8. Blowing Up Balloons the Easy Way

No. 9. Betty Goes Bananas!

No. 10. The Broncs Are Beautiful

> **BA–BE**

> **BI–BK**

> **BL–BO**

> **BR–BY**

Name _____   Date _____

Orders, Orders, Orders!

You can order a pizza and have it delivered.

You can order your dog to stop biting the couch.

And you can order the subjects in the list below so they are alphabetically **in order**.

DO IT . . . Number these subjects 1–42, with number 1 being the first item alphabetically and number 42 being the last item.

If you have several subjects that begin with the same letters, group them, then alphabetize by the letters that are different:

Asia	Aspirin	Assassins	Astronauts

_____ Botany	_____ Battles	_____ Archaeology
_____ Beagles	_____ Amphibians	_____ Bacon
_____ Bulimia	_____ Acid Rain	_____ Arizona
_____ Assassins	_____ Astronauts	_____ Art
_____ Aristotle	_____ Anthropology	_____ Asia
_____ Baseball	_____ Ants	_____ Bible
_____ Basketball	_____ Anatomy	_____ Bridges
_____ Atmosphere	_____ Adolescents	_____ Aspirin
_____ Antarctica	_____ Blood	_____ Anorexia
_____ Arab Countries	_____ Business	_____ Architects
_____ Buffalo	_____ Birds	_____ Biology
_____ Apples	_____ Atomic Bomb	_____ Bells
_____ Baby-sitters	_____ Abortion	_____ Athletes
_____ Bananas	_____ Automobiles	_____ Bees

What's in a Card

Library cards don't say much. But what they tell you is very important. Such as:

The CALL NUMBER . . .   Each book is assigned a number according to the Dewey decimal system; it's located at the top left corner of the library card.

The TITLE . . .   The book's title is printed on the card, but not underlined.

The AUTHOR . . .   Cards are filed by author's last name, alphabetically.

The PUBLISHER . . .   The name of the company that published the book is printed after the title.

The COPYRIGHT DATE . . .   like: c1989, or c1977

Number of PAGES . . .   like: 212p, or: 333p

PHOTOS or
ILLUSTRATIONS . . .   The word "photos" or "illus" or both words will be printed on the card if the book contains either of these items.

The book's SUMMARY . . .   Many cards tell in a few words what the book is about.

The parts of a library card are identified below.

(This happens to be a **Title** card).

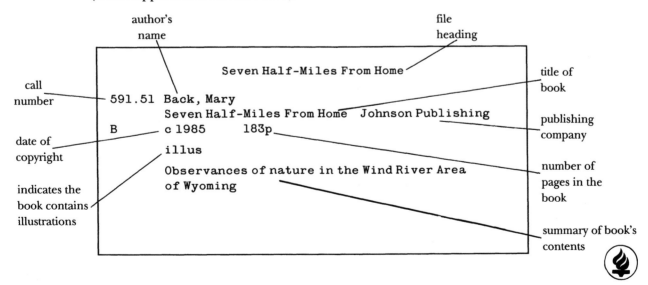

Three to One

When a library has three cards for every book, things can get cluttered. So some libraries use three separate card catalogs: one for **subject** cards, one for **title** cards, and another for **author** cards.

Example: Below are three cards identifying the same book. Look closely at the very top of each card: On the **subject** card, one word appears in capital letters; on the **author** card, the author's name is written on top; on the **title** card, the title comes at the top. These are called *file headings* and are the key words used to alphabetize books.

```
629.2    AUTOMOBILES
Sul      Sullivan, George
         Great racing cars/by George Sullivan; ill.
         with photographs. - Dodd, Mead, c1987.
         64 p.: ill., col. photos. - index.
         Summary: This book describes a wide variety
         of racing cars and the races in which they are used.
```
(Subject Card)

```
629.2
Sul      Sullivan, George
         Great racing cars/by George Sullivan; ill.
         with photographs. - Dodd, Mead, c1987.
         64 p.: ill., col. photos. - index.
         Summary: This book describes a wide variety
         of racing cars and the races in which they are used.
```

```
629.2    Great racing cars
Sul      Sullivan, George
         Great racing cars/by George Sullivan; ill.
         with photographs. - Dodd, Mead, c1987.
         64 p.: ill., col. photos. - index.
         Summary: This book describes a wide variety
         of racing cars and the races in which they are
         used.
         ISBN 0-396-08911-9
            1. Automobiles        2. Automobile racing
         I. Title
DOD-0754                               629.2
```
(Author Card)
(Title Card)

Fill in the Card

Below are two blank title cards with boxes drawn in them. Using the information located beside each card, put the file heading, the title, call number, author, and all other entries in their appropriate boxes.

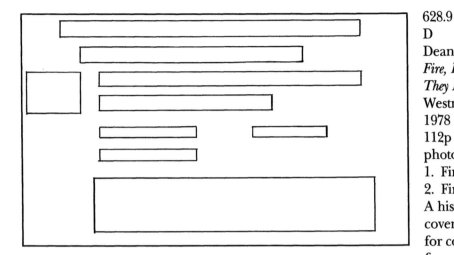

628.9
D
Dean, Anabel
Fire, How Do They Fight It?
Westminster
1978
112p
photos, ill.
1. Fire Prevention
2. Firefighting
A history of firefighting, covering techniques for combatting city fires, forest fires, and airport fires.

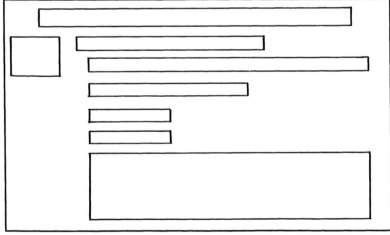

920
Gui
Campion, Nardi R.
Look to This Day
Little, Brown
1965
508p
Illus
Photos
1. Medicine/Biog.
The life and education of one of America's first female physicians: Connie Guion, M.D.

How to Write Reports

Do It Yourself

Using the information in the box below, write out a **subject** card, an **author** card, and a **title** card for this book on friendship.

Subject: FRIENDSHIP

Title: *Boy Friends, Girl Friends, Just Friends*

Author: Arlene Kramer Richards

Call number: 177
            R

Publisher: Atheneum

Copyright: 1979

No. of pages: 155

Illustrated with photos

Summary: An explanation of the pleasures, pains, and responsibilities of friendship in the high school years.

(continued)

Do It Yourself *(continued)*

Get That Number

Have you ever seen someone overcome by "locker trance"? The victim stands at his or her locker and stares at the door as if some new movie is playing there on a tiny invisible screen.

It can happen in the library too.

You can know the title page of a book, its author, its publisher, the number of pages, even its price, and still end up staring at a shelf of books as if some new movie is playing there on a tiny invisible screen.

That's called "number lock."

To avoid number lock and to get the book you want, you need two pieces of information:

1. The call number of your book.
2. The shelf marked with that call number.

The call number is located in the top left corner of any library card. Write this number and accompanying letters on a notecard and head for the "stacks" (shelves).

Nonfiction books are shelved in numerical order from the lowest numbers to the highest beginning at the top left of the shelf and running to the bottom right corner as shown below:

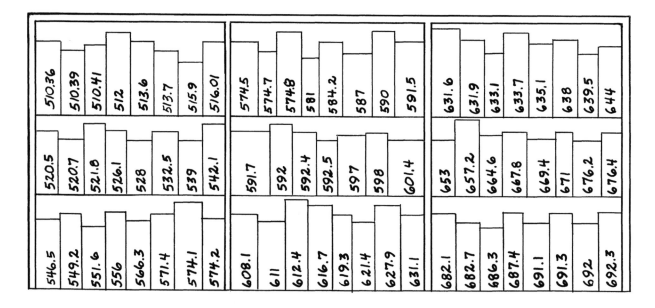

"Numberize"!

"**Numberizing**" is the art of putting library books in numerical order on a shelf. (Librarians can do this without batting an eye.)

Below are 24 titles and their call numbers. They are *not* in numerical order.

Arrange these works numerically by writing their numbers from lowest to highest onto the "books" drawn on the shelf below. The first and last ones are done for you.

200	In Search of Meaning		353.5	The Supreme Court
242	Set My Heart Free		292	Heroes and Monsters of Greek Myth
261.7	The Rebirth of America		365.973	America's Prisons
220.9	Atlas of the Bible		351.009	A Changing America
291	Great Classical Myths		342.522	Endure and Conquer
220.1	It Is No Dream		338	Grinding It Out
248.4	Ordering Your Private World		338.1	American Agriculture
291.63	Faith Made Them Champion		346.01	Search for Anna Fisher
335.4	Hitler's Counterfeit Reich		341	The Key to Peace
341.13	The UN and How It Works		340.023	Law and the New Woman
355	The American Military		353.03	The Growing Powers of the Presidency
337.8	Energy: An Issue of the '80's		364.973	Criminal Justice

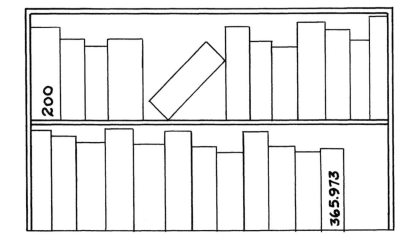

Name _____ Date _____

Last Step

People climb mountains for one main reason: to experience the thrill of that last step when they stand alone on the peak and look down at the earth.

Your last step in library research is when you walk up to the shelf and grab the one book you need out of the hundreds sitting there before you. But you can't make this final step without knowing which shelf holds your book. Here's how:

Shelves in the library have numbers posted on each end—for example: *571.45–679.64.* This means that all the books with call numbers from 571.45 to 679.64 are on that particular shelf.

Below are listed 22 books and their numbers, and above the books are three numbered shelves like ones you'd find in a library. Next to each book, write the letter of the shelf that would hold the book.

Example: __A__ 526.8 *Mapmaking*

Shelf A
```
510–
551.1
```

Shelf B
```
552–
610.5
```

Shelf C
```
611–
698.4
```

1. _____ 550 *Marvels of the Earth*
2. _____ 629.1309 *Early Airplanes*
3. _____ 582.16 *Trees of North America*
4. _____ 549.02 *The Rockhound's Manual*
5. _____ 613.6 *Survive: Don't Be a Victim*
6. _____ 560 *Guide to Fossils*
7. _____ 567.9 *Digging for Dinosaurs*
8. _____ 635 *Gardening for Food and Fun*
9. _____ 646.21 *I Love to Sew*
10. _____ 534.5 *Silent Sound*
11. _____ 685 *Cowboy Craft*
12. _____ 617.1027 *Sports Medicine Book*

13. _____ 526.8 *Mapmaking*
14. _____ 539.76 *History of the Atomic Bomb*
15. _____ 574.09 *A Short History of Biology*
16. _____ 553.809 *Gems and Precious Stones*
17. _____ 574.5 *The Edge of the Sea*
18. _____ 610 *The Medicine Show*
19. _____ 519 *Camouflage in Nature*
20. _____ 621.384 *Audio and Radio*
21. _____ 658.4 *Women Like Us*
22. _____ 612.84 *The Eye: Window on the World*

Next of Kin

Some books are related, like cousins.

If you're doing a report on earthquakes, for instance, and you get the call number 551.2 for a book called *The Restless Earth*, you will find when you step up to the shelf that several books related to the subject have the *same* call number.

NOW WHAT?

Check the three letters beneath the call number. These are the first three letters of the author's last name.

Example: 551.2   *Earthquakes*
            Hal

            551.2   *The Restless Earth*
            Lau

            551.2   *The Story of the Earth*
            Mat

Books related by topic that have the same call number are alphabetized by the first three letters of the author's last name.

Below are 10 related books and their call numbers. Order the books alphabetically as they would appear on the shelf by placing a number 1 next to the book that would come first, a number 2 by the book that would come second, and so on.

_____ 748.2 *Dig Those Crazy Bottles*   _____ 748.2 *Custard Glass*
      Kau   Bra

_____ 748.2 *Art Glass Nouveau*   _____ 748.2 *Excursions in Old Glass*
      Gro   Mil

_____ 748.2 *Milk Glass*   _____ 748.2 *Stiegel Glass*
      Bel   Hun

_____ 748.2 *Glassblowing: A Search for Form* _____ 748.2 *Creative Glassblowing*
      Lit   Ham

_____ 748.2 *Early American Pattern Glass*   _____ 748.2 *The Mouth-Blown Bottle*
      Met   Ken

Name _____ Date _____

Everything in Its Place

Libraries are like shopping malls—certain things are found in certain places. You don't walk into the pet store in a mall and ask for computer disks. And you shouldn't go into the reference section of a library looking for *Teen* magazine. Everything has its place!

The map on the next page has numbered sections: #1 is the circulation desk (the librarian's work station), #2 is the card catalog, #3 is the reference section, and so on.

Below are listed 15 sources of information. On the line next to each source, write the number of the library section that would hold that source.

Example: __3__ *The Encyclopaedia Britannica*

1. _____ *The World Book Encyclopedia*

2. _____ individual photos of our national parks

3. _____ the novel *Where the Red Fern Grows*

4. _____ a copy of an article from *The New York Times* newspaper dated July 14, 1951

5. _____ *National Geographic* magazine

6. _____ the comic section of your local newspaper

7. _____ a book that tells how to fry cheese

8. _____ *Guinness Book of Records*

9. _____ a book that teaches bicycle repair

10. _____ the collected short stories of Edgar Allan Poe

11. _____ a book about the desert country of Australia

12. _____ *Webster's New World Dictionary*

13. _____ a biography of Annie Oakley

14. _____ a library card on the subject PUMPKINS

15. _____ a book about hunting in British Columbia

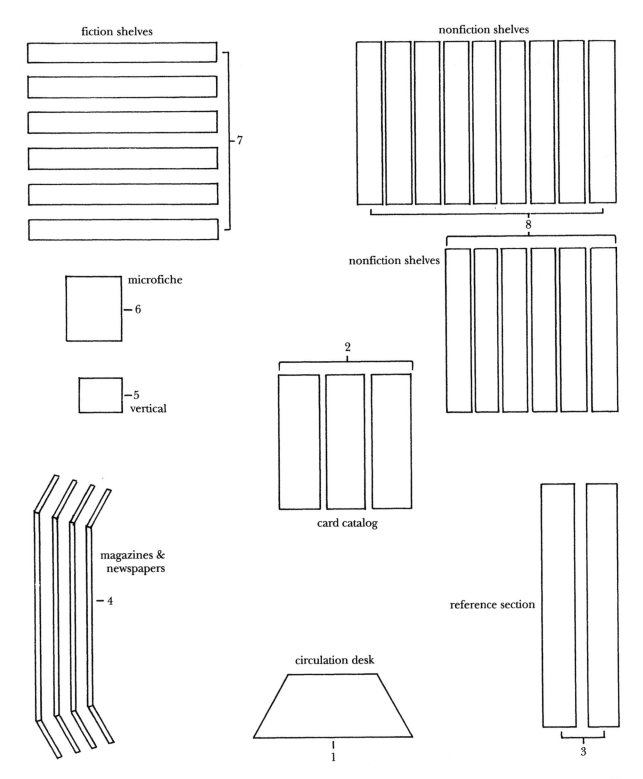

fiction shelves

nonfiction shelves

7

microfiche

6

5
vertical

nonfiction shelves

8

2

card catalog

magazines &
newspapers

4

reference section

3

circulation desk

1

Library Tips

To get something from a department store, you find the store you want, you walk in and find where the goods are stored, you select from the goods on the shelf, and if you have any trouble with your selection, you ask for help.

Libraries are similar, but easier.

All the "merchandise" in a library is coded, alphabetized, stored in easy-to-find places, and free. Here are a few tips to make your library "shopping" easier.

Tip #1: Remember that all libraries are unique, so don't expect things to be in the exact same places from library to library. Ask for HELP if you need it.

Tip #2: Many libraries have films, records, cassettes, slides, compact disks, and VCR tapes that can be checked out (or rented) and used for research.

Tip #3: Copy machines are available in most libraries, and for a few cents per page you can get information from a magazine without signing out the issue.

Tip #4: FAX machines are also available in many libraries. If you find a magazine article that you need, but your library is out of that particular issue, your librarian can call another library and have the article sent over the phone lines using the FAX machine. There is sometimes a charge for this service.

Tip #5: Librarians will love you if you DON'T reshelve books once you've taken them off the shelves because you might put them back in the wrong order.

Tip #6: You are not the only person using the library. If a book is out, put your name on the waiting list or go to another library, possibly a college library, for a copy.

Tip #7: Be aware that college and university libraries use a different system for cataloging and shelving books. It's called the Library of Congress system. Ask the librarian for help in finding material.

Tip #8: YOU ARE NOT ALONE. Libraries are happy to help with any book-finding that needs to be done.

CHAPTER 3:

GATHERING INFORMATION

Name _____   Date _____

Starting Out

You've gathered armloads of books, films, newspapers, magazines, and encyclopedia articles that deal with your topic. You're excited, but maybe a little worried too. How are you going to get a finished report out of all of this?

First: Read each piece—but not necessarily every word. Just read the details that best explain or describe your topic. This is called **skimming**.

Second: Take careful **notes** by . . .

- writing down the main ideas in an article or chapter.

- taking down exact quotes from experts.

- writing the title, author, and page number of the magazine or book.

Third: Organize the notes around a **master plan** (sometimes called an **outline**).

Fourth: Write a **rough draft**.

Fifth: **Revise** the paper.

Sixth: **Rewrite** the report so it can be presented to others.

Skimming Is Easy

You're feeling smug. Everyone is wandering around the library looking for report material while you sit at a library table piled with books, magazines, and newspaper articles on a very good report topic: BOREDOM.

It's a nice feeling, but there's a problem. One of your books contains 300 pages. Another has 400 pages. There are three magazine articles, three newspapers, and a pamphlet from the vertical file staring you in the face.

How are you going to read it all?

The answer is one word: **skimming**.

Have you ever scraped the thick brown skin off the top of a dish of chocolate pudding so you could get to the good stuff below?

That's **skimming**.

Skimming works for books too. If you've got a 400-page psychology book that has one chapter on BOREDOM, why read the whole book? Just go to that chapter and skim the subheadings (in dark print). Then look for a few details under each subhead and jot them down. Use one 3 × 5 card for each subhead and skim along till you finish the chapter.

That's all there is to it.

Watch for Bullets

Some writers make it easy for you to skim by highlighting certain information with **bullets.** No, they don't shoot the page. They use a heavy black dot next to each item that they think is important.

Conflicting interpretations

Consider the case of Molly, a high school student accused of plagiarizing a paper entitled "Who's to Blame for Pearl Harbor?" Molly merely reworded the ideas of a magazine article on the subject, her history teacher charged, without once giving credit where credit was due. "But I rewrote it. I cut out some stuff and added some new stuff," Molly argued. "That's not plagiarism."

Oh, yes, it is, according to the school's (and the Random House dictionary's) definition of plagiarism: "To steal (the language, ideas, or thoughts) from (another), representing them as one's own original work." The definition simply means that an author's words *and ideas* are his property and anyone who borrows those words or ideas must acknowledge her source.

But there are some cardinal rules to be culled from Gabrielle's [mentioned earlier in the original article] and Molly's misfortunes. All students, no matter where they go to school, must remember these principles:

• Intent to plagiarize is irrelevant at most schools, and, in any case, lack of intent is very difficult to prove. You must assume that if what got in your paper was copied from another source that's not acknowledged, you've plagiarized. If you take notes in researching a paper, be sure to carefully note the source of all information—then credit the source for anything you use. The argument "I thought these were my own words, I didn't realize they came from a book" won't wash.

• Claiming "I only copied one sentence here or one paragraph there" is no defense. *Any* uncredited lifting of another person's words or ideas—no matter how small—constitutes plagiarism. In a 1980 survey of students at Iowa State University, in Iowa City, only 44 percent felt it was dishonest to copy a few sentences from a source without footnoting. Yet technically, had that other 56 percent done what they apparently condoned, they would have committed plagiarism.

• "But I put it in my own words" is also no defense. Some students believe that careful para-phrasing gives them carte blanche to plunder another's work. They forget that *ideas* as well as words are the property of the person who created them. Suppose you had devised a theory for a political science term paper on why President Reagan won such a sweeping victory in the last election. Another student read your paper and presented the exact theory but in his own words. If he neglected to credit your paper as the source of the idea, he plagiarized.

• You must acknowledge every appearance of borrowed material. Gabrielle was tragically mistaken in thinking that five footnotes would cover fifty borrowed passages.

• Whether or not a source is copyrighted is also immaterial. "Okay, so I copied from a friend's paper," one high school sophomore admitted. "That's not plagiarism. It has never been published; it's not copyrighted." But that student had indeed plagiarized. Unacknowledged borrowing from any outside source—published or unpublished, written by a distinguished authority or by a classmate—is plagiarism.

(continued)

How to Write Reports

Watch for Bullets (continued)

Skim the passage on the previous page taken from an article called "Plagiarism" by Carol Felsenthal in *Seventeen* magazine, May 1985. Copy the subtitle from the top of the first column, then write the sentence that comes directly after each bullet.

Subtitle _____

Bullet #1 _____

_____

Bullet #2 _____

_____

Bullet #3 _____

_____

Bullet #4 _____

_____

Bullet #5 _____

_____

Bulleting

Bullets are easy to spot; they stick out like black pimples. Read the two versions of the paragraph below and see which is easier to skim.

Giving a party doesn't have to be a chore. You can have a good time without driving yourself crazy with details if you take a few precautions.

First, ask each person invited to bring some food or refreshment. Don't spend hours making special goodies that will be devoured 10 minutes after the party starts.

Second, ask three people to bring music. You can't be expected to get enough music together on your own to make everybody happy.

Third, build the party around a theme: the 1950's or 1960's or the Civil War. People won't worry then about what to wear or what to do.

Fourth, set a definite time to end the party. Some people will hang around till dawn, if you let them.

Fifth, get help to clean up half an hour before "quitting time." Wash the glasses, plates, and silverware, and put the punch bowl away. Then vacuum. Your parents will love you and will let you sleep the next day.

BULLETED VERSION

To have an easy-going party with no hassles, do the following:

- Have friends bring food or beverage.

- Ask three people to bring their tapes and discs to add variety to the music.

- Plan the party around a theme to make it easy for fancy dressers.

- Set a definite quitting time.

- Clean up half an hour before the party is supposed to end.

WHEN SKIMMING, ZERO IN ON BULLETS. YOU CAN'T MISS.

78 *How to Write Reports*

Zero In

Read the paragraph below, then bullet the information by putting one important detail next to each bullet. The first one is done for you.

Scientific principles are formed by following a strict process involving five basic steps. First, a scientist observes what is happening. He or she will note facts in a notebook or say them into a tape recorder so there is a record of what took place. Second, the scientist states a hypothesis, or educated guess as to what the observations might mean. Then an experiment is set up to see if the educated guess is right or wrong. Next, the experiment is performed by other scientists to see if the hypothesis is correct. And finally, a conclusion can be formed based on the results of all the experiments.

BULLETED VERSION

Scientific principles and laws are formed by following a simple five-step process:

Bullet #1 _Observe and record what is happening._

Bullet #2 _____

Bullet #3 _____

Bullet #4 _____

Bullet #5 _____

Bullets aren't the only way to organize material. Read more about it on the next page.

Name _____ Date _____

Food for Thought

Bullets aren't the only skimming tools that writers use to highlight information.

Subheadings can also do the trick.

If you're not sure what a subhead is, look on any menu. A restaurant will list the breakfast items in one column, the lunch items in another column, the dinner foods in another place, and the desserts somewhere else. By skimming the **subheads** you know whether you're reading off the right column. (I know. Only one column for you . . . desserts, right?)

Anyone trying to read the menu below would get indigestion. HELP!

List the items under their proper **subheadings**.

Menu: Scrambled eggs and ham, chocolate pie, ice cream, jumbo shrimp, cake, pancakes, waffles, sirloin steak, apple pie, baked trout, braised duck, roast leg of lamb, grilled pork chops, French toast, wheat toast, and pineapple sundae.

BREAKFAST	**DINNER**	**DESSERT**

Skim It!

The best place to **skim** is in a restaurant, because the results go right to your tummy.

Take the menu below, for example, from the Harman Ranch Restaurant in Tempe, Arizona. (Don't be fooled by the prices—this was printed years ago.) Eleven items are listed on the page. Read as if you were going to order something, then write your selection on the line provided next to the menu.

(selection)

You probably didn't read every word on the menu. You **skimmed** over the small print and read the bold, dark words that named such items as **Cowgirl Steak**. Your brain enjoys skimming. It will pick out the easy-to-see words and skim over smaller words that are hard to read. That way you can find out what's on a piece of paper without spending precious time reading every word.

How to Write Reports

Subheads, Where Are You?

A **subhead** is not someone who has spent too many hours under the Arctic Ocean in a submarine.

A **subhead** announces what's ahead in a paragraph or in an article.

Find the subheads in the article below and write them on the lines provided. (They are not in dark, heavy type. So look carefully)

Fundraising for You and Your Organization

Fundraising is an important part of many teenage organizations in America. To take trips, help the underprivileged during holiday seasons, or make contributions to the community, teens have to raise money. It is never easy. It is an activity that takes planning, salesmanship, and hard work.

Planning Your Fundraiser

To prepare for a successful fundraising activity you must first get support from the entire group. Two or three people cannot sell enough items or raffle off enough turkeys to meet the needs of the project. Next, you must pick a method for raising funds: selling cards or magazines, raffling something off, or a community activity like washing cars. Finally, you must set a date for the project to begin and a date for it to end.

Selling Door to Door

To raise funds, many groups take products door to door in their communities. Here salesmanship is important. You must not be too pushy, but you must not give up in despair either, when a customer says, "No thanks." Also, always go with someone when you sell door to door.

Hard Work Pays Off

The first thing a group of teens has to do is agree to stay with the project till the funds are raised. This commitment is essential because there are products to distribute, streets to cover, money to be accounted for, prizes to be awarded, and products to be delivered. It is not easy. But it can be done for the benefit of any teen organization and for the community at large.

subhead _____

_____

subhead _____

_____

subhead _____

_____

subhead _____

_____

More Subheads

Below are three separate paragraphs written as if they are one. Circle the first three words of the *first sentence* in each paragraph. Then, on the line provided, write a two- or three-word *subhead* that tells what each paragraph is about.

The morning of April 19, 1775, dawned bright and bloody in Lexington, Massachusetts. A handful of Colonists stood in the way of hundreds of British soldiers who were marching to Concord. When the two groups met they exchanged gunfire. Eight Colonists lay dead when the smoke finally cleared. The Revolutionary War had begun. Some people say Richard Sears, founder of the Sears, Roebuck, Company, was a genius. Others say he was a copycat, because his famous mail-order catalog that was mailed to millions of American farmers in the late 1800's and early 1900's was actually invented years before by Montgomery Ward in 1873. Sears wrote all his own catalog ads and improved the catalog in lots of other ways, but he can't get credit for inventing the great selling idea. That honor must stay with Mr. Ward. The first snowfall of the year is almost as exciting as Christmas morning. It's as if the sky has dropped an elegant gift on your front lawn, all wrapped in white. Yards and trees and fences and houses all take on a clean, fresh look. Clothes that are hung out to dry on the line and are brought into the house afterward smell like sweet, cool raindrops. Trees that were bare and cold are now dressed in fine, thick layers of white. And at night the view out the living room window of the snow sifting down like fine diamonds through the yellow light of the street lamp on the corner makes life seem, just for a moment, like a real Christmas card.

subhead _____

_____

subhead _____

_____

subhead _____

_____

How to Write Reports

Do It Yourself

Below are two lists.

Read each one, then create a subhead that would summarize or include all the items on the list.

Then write the subhead on the line.

Check the example for help.

Example:
a. Turn on the oven to 350 degrees.
b. Tear the top off the box.
c. Pour cake mix into a bowl.
d. Add eggs, flour, water, and oil.
e. Beat into smooth batter.
f. Rub margarine on inside of cake pan.
g. Place in oven for 30 minutes.
h. Take out cake and let it cool.
i. Apply frosting.

subhead _*Baking a cake*_____

List #1:
a. Decide where you want to go.
b. Buy your ticket.
c. Get to airport 1½ hours early.
d. Check in your baggage at the counter.
e. When your flight number is called, give the flight attendant your ticket.
f. Get on the plane and buckle into your seat.

subhead _____

List #2:
a. Call the hospital to see who really needs a visitor.
b. Send a card to that person telling who you are and asking when you can visit.
c. Buy a flower or a magazine or book to bring as a gift.
d. Dress nicely and wear a smile.
e. Ask questions about family and friends and favorite foods and hobbies, etc.
f. Say goodbye and wish the patient a speedy recovery.

subhead _____

Find the Subhead

Below are two paragraphs.

Read each one and write a subhead on the line provided.

Paragraph 1   To start a service business, you need to first find out what people need: cars washed, windows cleaned, yards raked, or pets walked, for example. Then you must decide which service you would like to perform. Next, look at your schedule to see when the best time would be to do the work. Then contact customers who live close to you and give them a business card stating your name, occupation, business times, and prices. Stay by the phone so you can take appointments. Then do the best job you possibly can.

subhead _____

Paragraph 2   To get the most from your study time you must write your assignment clearly in a notebook along with the date on which the work is due. Then set a time, say 6:00 P.M., when you will start to work. Set up a place with a desk or table, a lamp, paper, pens, computer, typewriter, and whatever other equipment you need to do a good job. Cut out all distractions. Finish the assignments that are due the soonest. Don't move on to the second piece of work till the first one is finished. Finally, make a finished copy of your work and place it in a notebook or in the appropriate section of your folder. Sleep well!

subhead _____

Name _____   Date _____

Skimming Practice

Skim the article below, then copy the subhead and the first sentence from each paragraph on the lines provided.

Slavery Starts the War

Among the many reasons for the Civil War, slavery was the most obvious. Capturing, whipping, and chaining people to plows to work until they dropped was unthinkable to many citizens of the North, while many citizens in the Southern states believed in slavery and claimed that without slaves the economy of the South would dry up. This clash of beliefs led to many arguments and con-flicts. And no one knew where it would end.

Abolitionists Fuel the Fire

Citizens who were violently against slavery were called "abolitionists." Their speeches and books and news articles raised support for the antislav-ery movement in the North. People marched in the streets, wrote letters to the president, and published newspapers that told of the "sin of slavery." Many slave owners in the South became angry and threatened to break away from the Union. Slavery was their way of life, they said.

The War Begins

Finally, in December of 1860, South Carolina broke from the United States. By January of 1861 shots had been fired at a ship sent from Washington, D.C., with reinforcements to Fort Sum-ter, and the war had unofficially begun.

Paragraph 1 _____

_____

_____

Paragraph 2 _____

_____

_____

Paragraph 3 _____

_____

_____

How to Write Reports

From Subheads to Notes

Skimming an article without taking **notes** is like taking a picture with no film in the camera—a waste of time!

To make skimming work for you, jot down on 3 × 5 index cards the subheadings or topic sentences (first sentences) of paragraphs in an article. Use one card for each subhead. Then take each sentence under the subhead and pick out the main facts, dates, or quotes and jot them down on the card beneath the subhead. Use brief language. Don't copy the sentence word for word.

Example: Skim the following article, then look at the "notecards" below. Notice how the subheads are written at the top, and the important details are listed underneath them.

What's a Wave?

A wave is energy in motion, but in a pattern. A wave goes only so high, then curves and drops down only so low, then curves up again, drops down, then curves up once more to form a pattern. This pattern is called a WAVE.

Kinds of Waves

There are three main kinds of waves: light waves, sound waves, and water waves. The waves that pour out of your stereo are sound waves. The electromagnetic waves coming from the sun are called light waves. And the waves that hold up a surfboard are called water waves. Without these different kinds of waves, life on Earth would be unlivable.

Uses of Waves

We use waves to do everything: cook food, watch TV, or play the guitar. Sound waves carry our voices through the air to our friends' ears. Electromagnetic rays bring the sun's energy to plants on Earth so they can grow. They also carry our favorite songs through the atmosphere from radio stations. And they allow doctors to see pictures of broken bones beneath the skin (X rays). Nobody gets very far on Earth without the help of these powerful waves.

```
What's a Wave?
  1. motion
  2. curve
  3. pattern
```

```
Kinds of Waves
  1. light (sunshine)
  2. sound
  3. water
```

```
Uses of Waves
  1. carry voices
  2. plant growth (sunlight)
  3. radio communication
  4. X rays (see through skin)
```

How to Write Reports

Name _____   Date _____

Good Notes

Notes are like telegrams.

They're written in short, clipped language, not long, detailed sentences.

Read the paragraph on rain forests below taken from an article titled "Paradise Lost" by Suzanne McCabe, in *Junior Scholastic* magazine, April 1989. Then write three facts found in the paragraph next to the numbers on the "notecard." (The first fact has been recorded for you.)

The rain forests of South America are vanishing under a cloud of black smoke. People who want the land are burning the forests to clear it for farms. In fact, in 1987, 27 million acres were burned off. With so many trees being burned, the carbon dioxide level in the atmosphere is rising, which can cause the sun's heat to be trapped over the earth. This is called "global warming" and can make life impossible here on earth.

Burning the rain forests:

1. (why)   *To clear land for farms*

2. (how much)

3. (problem)

4. (problem)

Keep Skimming

Read the material below on exercise, taken from *The Sports Medicine Book*, by Mirkin and Hoffman. Then write a subhead on each of the blank "notecards" on the next page (the first one has been done for you below) and list two or three pieces of information on each card.

Myths About Exercise
People say and believe things about exercise that simply aren't true. Here are three myths: You don't have to do much to be physically fit, exercise can enlarge your heart and harm you, and exercising in the cold can freeze your lungs. Actually, exercising three times a week for at least one-half hour is a minimum for staying healthy. That takes time and hard work. After exercising over a period of a year, your heart is stronger, as any other muscle would be, and pumps more blood with fewer beats per minute. And as for exercising in the cold, go for it! Along with your winter coat and pants, you'll need to cover your face, hands, and feet, but your lungs will be okay.

Rewards of Exercise
Exercise has several benefits. First, it calms you down and makes you feel "mellow." Second, it increases the blood flow to your brain, which provides more oxygen to your brain cells and helps your whole body run more smoothly. Third, your appetite for sweets and salts and fats will lessen. And fourth, you will sleep better and wake up more refreshed.

Cautions About Exercise
Don't overwork when you begin an exercise program. When you feel pain or you get dizzy or can't breathe, stop. Pain is a signal that the body is in some sort of difficulty. Start slowly. Rest often. Slowly, over a period of months, increase the length and speed of your workouts.

Myths About Exercise

1. Don't need to do much (but need 3 times/week for ½ hour).

2. Can enlarge heart/cause harm (but heart gets stronger like other muscles).

3. Freeze lungs in cold weather (not true . . . but face, hands, and feet need protection).

Keep Skimming *(continued)*

From Bullets to Notes

There's another way to find subheads when taking notes on a subject—look for **bullets**. All you need to do is give a short title to each paragraph that is bulleted, using a separate card for each bullet. Include any details—dates, amounts, facts, reasons, or examples—that explain the topic further.

Write a subhead and details for each of the bulleted paragraphs below in the cards provided.

Stress comes in many forms. Let's say your family decides to move—you might feel stressed about making new friends and living in a new town. Or maybe you decide to try an after-school job—you could feel stressed about the interview.

These situations can be handled more easily by following two suggestions.
● Realize there are things beyond your control. If your family moves, you must go along, so don't brood over the decision.

Instead, find some creative ways to help the family and yourself through this stressful time—get brochures and books from the library and show your brothers and sisters how beautiful the new place really is; write to the Chamber of Commerce in the town where you'll be living and ask for information about schools, stores, parks, and activity centers. Don't spend your valuable time worrying. Do something positive.

● Think Positively. Dwelling on the negative side of things takes energy—too much energy. Invest some time looking at all the positive aspects of the situation. Tell yourself that you are going to make the situation work for you and not against you. You have the power to control your thoughts, and your actions. Don't burn up energy by putting yourself down. After all, *you* haven't changed—the situation has.

Name _____ Date _____

Note Patterns

What do reports and ice cream cones have in common? There are lots of different kinds!

You can report on . . .   PEOPLE

PLACES

EVENTS

ANIMALS

PLANTS

OCCUPATIONS

HISTORICAL PERIODS

INVENTIONS

TRENDS

SPORTS

HOBBIES

And more . . . !

But different reports require different notes, and if you know what these types of notes are, you'll make your reporting life a lot easier.

Example: A report on the life of Sandra Day O'Connor, the first female Supreme Court justice, should have notes on:

Childhood

Family

Education

Career

Achievements

Struggles

Future Plans

The above list can provide a PATTERN for your notes when you report on *any* person, no matter who it is.

You should use one card for each aspect of the person's life—one card for CHILDHOOD, one card for EDUCATION, another card for FAMILY, and so on. That way, when you write your outline, you could set the cards in the order you want and take the dates and names and events down as you write.

More Patterns

Below are patterns for six types of reports. Each is a little different because each subject requires different information.

When you do a report using any of these patterns, each heading should be on a separate card. For PLACE, for example, write "Economy" on one card, "Climate" on another card, and so on. Then, when you write the report, you can stack the cards in the order you want and start writing.

PLACE (state, city, nation, national park, island)

- Economy
- Type of Government
- Climate
- Plants
- Animals
- Natural Wonders
- Natural Resources
- History
  a. famous people
  b. famous events

HUMAN-MADE THINGS
(car, stereo, sandwich)

- Definition or Explanation
- Inventor/Creator
- Uses
- Structure: How is it put together?
- Function: What has been its impact on modern life?

CREATURE (whale, ant, snake, bird, fish, ?)

- Definition of creature (Different types)
- Habits
  a. reproduction
  b. food gathering
  c. migration?
- History of creature's development
- Environment (where it lives)
- Future: threatened by extinction?

SPORTS/HOBBIES
(golf, volleyball, skateboarding)

- History: When was the sport invented?
  Who invented it?
  Who are some famous players?
- Function: What are the rules?
  What skills are needed?
  What importance does it have for people?
- Future: What will the sport be like in 20 years?

(continued)

More Patterns *(continued)*

NATURAL THINGS

(caves, volcanoes, stars, microwaves, hurricanes)

- Definition/Explanation
- HOW do they work or act?
- WHERE are they located?
- WHO knows most about them?
- WHAT dangers do they pose?
- WHAT good do they do?
- HOW have people used them to make life on earth better?

EVENTS (war, social movements, explorations)

- WHEN did they occur?
- WHERE did they occur?
- WHO participated?
- HOW did they begin?
- HOW did they end?
- WHAT happened after?

Name _____   Date _____

Make a Note Pattern

Look at the headings listed below.

Whenever you write a "biographical report" on someone, you can use these same headings to help organize the information you find after reading your books, magazines, and newspapers or after watching a videotape.

HINT: Use at least one card for each heading.

Subject: (Name of the person you are writing about)

CHILDHOOD .... Born:

Lived:

School:

FAMILY .... Sisters/Brothers:

Father/Mother:

Spouse/Children:

EDUCATION .... School:

College:

Self-Taught:

ACHIEVEMENTS .... Prizes:

Titles:

Impact on the World:

STRUGGLES .... Illness:

Death of Family

 Member/Friend:

Handicaps?

CAREER ....

Name _____   Date _____

More Notes

Read the two paragraphs below about Abe Lincoln. On notecard #1 list the important details from the first paragraph. Then on notecard #2 write the details from the second paragraph.

(—from *Lincoln: A Photobiography,* by Russell Freedman, Houghton Mifflin, New York, 1987)

Abe Lincoln was a poor, tough, uneducated boy who faced a life of hard work and difficulty. His first home was a dirt-floored cabin near Hodgenville, Kentucky. He was born there in February of 1809. Two years later his family moved north a few miles to another cabin beside Knob Creek. Then when Abe was 7 years old, his father moved them to Indiana, where they lived in a three-sided shelter along a riverbank through the winter of 1817. By the following year Abe's mother had died of "milk sickness."

By age 9 Abe was doing man's work around the homestead. He split logs into fence rails to earn money for the family. He shoveled manure, built hog pens, and cleared land by chopping trees and pulling stumps.

He learned to read and write and became hooked on books. He'd walk miles to borrow a book, then walk back to return it and borrow another. By age 17 he had been to see his first big city: New Orleans, Louisiana. There he witnessed the selling of human beings as slaves, a sight he never forgot.

#1 CHILDHOOD

#2 CHILDHOOD

Name _____ Date _____

Take Note

Read the paragraphs below about Washington State. Then on the "notecards," jot down a few essential facts under each subhead. Hint: You could use these subheads for reports about *countries* too, like Canada, Japan, or Australia.

The state of Washington has a climate for everyone. If you like wet, rainy winters, you can live on the west coast between the acific Ocean and the Cascade Mountains. If you want lots of snow and frosty fall mornings, you can live in the foothills of the mountains. If you like hot, dry summers and long autumns, you would enjoy the high plains in the east where farmers grow grains and fruit, especially wheat and apples.

The natural resources of Washington are favorable too. Huge mountains like Mt. Rainier rise into the clouds for 14,000 feet, luring people to climb and hike along their broad shoulders. The Columbia River, carrying more water than any other river in the United States except the Mississippi, drops 1,200 feet on its 1,200-mile journey to the ocean down through canyons and over 7 dams that make Washington the hydroelectric power-producing giant of the nation. Great harbors produce fish by the ton, and forests full of giant cedar, pine, hemlock, and spruce cover half of the state. There are 3 national parks, 12 state parks, and over a dozen historical sites for people to visit.

Because of all these resources and the variety of climates, over 4 million people now live in Washington, including 60,000 Native Americans from several tribes. These people work in all kinds of jobs like aircraft manufacturing, computer software marketing, logging, farming, banking, fishing, and mining. In fact, Washington State produces over $66 billion worth of foreign trade each year, with Japan as the primary customer. There are 500 computer software companies in Washington, along with many biotechnology firms, and the nation's largest commercial aircraft company, Boeing Aircraft, which employs over 60,000 people.

```
┌─────────────────────────────┐   ┌─────────────────────────────┐
│ CLIMATE                     │   │ NATURAL RESOURCES           │
│                             │   │                             │
│                             │   │                             │
│                             │   │                             │
│                             │   │                             │
│                             │   │                             │
└─────────────────────────────┘   └─────────────────────────────┘

        ┌─────────────────────────────┐
        │ ECONOMY                     │
        │                             │
        │                             │
        │                             │
        │                             │
        └─────────────────────────────┘
```

How to Write Reports

Fill in the Cards

Read the paragraphs below based on an article in *Discover* magazine called, "The Little Waves That Could," by Mark Roman, pages 54–60, November 1989.

After reading the article, make notes on the three "cards" provided.

Microwaves are waves of energy that travel so fast you can't see them. They are produced by devices called "magnetrons" invented by the Raytheon Corporation in the 1940's.

Microwaves were first used for radar during World War II. But then an accident happened. A researcher was standing next to a magnetron when suddenly a candy bar in his pocket melted. He thought other foods might be heated with microwaves, so he held some popcorn in front of the magnetron and POW! It wasn't long (1952) before the first microwave oven was put on the market. It was almost 6 feet tall.

Microwaves heat food by spinning the water molecules within food end over end, 2.4 billion times a second. This vibration causes friction which creates heat which spreads to surrounding molecules all through the food. The reason some microwaved food feels hotter in the center is because the air at the outer edge of a potato, for instance, is cooler and heat moves from the potato to the cool air. The center, meanwhile, is surrounded by warmed molecules so it stays hotter. But the food is basically heated all at the same time using microwaves.

Other uses for microwaves are being discovered by researchers in medicine. Lately, cancer tumors have been heated with microwaves, and the cancerous cells are killed by the intense, quick heat. This works well because cancer tumors do not have blood capillaries to carry healing antibodies to the burned area. So the tumors "die."

```
┌─────────────────────────┐   ┌─────────────────────────┐
│ Definition              │   │ Function (How it works) │
│                         │   │                         │
│                         │   │                         │
│                         │   │                         │
│                         │   │                         │
│                         │   │                         │
│                         │   │                         │
└─────────────────────────┘   └─────────────────────────┘

        ┌─────────────────────────┐
        │ Uses                    │
        │                         │
        │                         │
        │                         │
        │                         │
        │                         │
        └─────────────────────────┘
```

How to Write Reports

Picture These Notes

Read the paragraphs below about photography. Then on the "notecards" provided, jot down the details you might use in a report on this interesting hobby. Don't write out complete sentences. Use short phrases. Use a dash (—) instead of the word *was* or *is*.

Example: Niepce—1st photograph—1826.

Photography is a combination of chemistry and light. A substance called "silver salt" becomes darker when light hits it. So if you hold up an apple in front of a piece of film that's coated with silver salts, all the area blocked by the apple will be white and the rest of the paper where light was able to reach will be dark. This is how you make a permanent image otherwise known as a photograph.

The first photograph was made in 1826 by a French physicist named Niepce. The photo still exists, but it's not like the clear, black and white photos we have today. Then a man named Daguerre improved the process and made clear, lasting photos using mercury vapor to develop the images onto paper. Later, during the Civil War, photography became extremely popular in America because a fellow named Mathew Brady made thousands of photos of men fighting and dying, and showed people how powerful photography can be. In modern times, Margaret Bourke-White changed the face of newspapers and magazines around the world with her vivid pictures of war during the 1940's.

To be a good photographer you need to understand how light and shadow work; you need to find interesting subjects viewed from creative angles; and you need a good, sturdy camera that doesn't require a lot of gadgets. The best way to get started is to take a course in photography if possible. Otherwise, read books, magazines, and journals in the library. Then talk to family members and friends who are "camera buffs" or visit with the photographer at your local newspaper. Then take dozens and dozens of photos.

```
┌─────────────────────────────┐    ┌─────────────────────────────┐
│ Explanation                 │    │ Famous Photographers        │
│                             │    │                             │
│                             │    │                             │
│                             │    │                             │
│                             │    │                             │
│                             │    │                             │
│                             │    │                             │
└─────────────────────────────┘    └─────────────────────────────┘

          ┌─────────────────────────────┐
          │ Getting Started             │
          │                             │
          │                             │
          │                             │
          │                             │
          │                             │
          │                             │
          └─────────────────────────────┘
```

The Master Plan

Having a pile of notecards on your desk is like having a pile of puzzle pieces on a table—the pieces make sense only when they are connected to each other.

You, the writer, must do the connecting when it comes to organizing notes into a report that makes sense and presents a complete "picture."

But how?

Use the headings from your notecards (which were taken from the subheadings of paragraphs in the articles you skimmed) and list them on a sheet of paper. Leave space for a few details under each heading. Mark the headings with Roman numerals, the main details with capital letters, and the subdetails with numbers. This will result in a **master plan** for your report that you can easily follow when you write the paragraphs that will make up your report. Notes on the subject of photography might result in a master plan like this:

I. Explanation
    A. Silver salt gets darker when light hits it.
    B. Coat film with silver salt.
    C. Place object between light source and film.
    D. Area around object will be dark on film.
    E. Result is a permanent image of object on film.

II. Famous Photographers
    A. Niepce—1st photo—1826 in France.
    B. Daguerre—clearer photos with mercury vapor.
    C. Mathew Brady—Civil War.
    D. Margaret Bourke-White—brought WWII home.

III. Getting Started
    A. Understand light/shadow effects on subjects.
    B. Find interesting subjects, creative angles.
    C. Need simple, sturdy camera.
    D. Take course in photography.
    E. Read journals, books, magazines.
    F. Meet professional photographers.
    G. Take lots of pictures (practice, practice).

Make a Plan

Making a **master plan** is nothing new.

When you plan a party, for example, you set up categories: *food, music, guest list, games, prizes,* etc. Then you list items under each category: Food—soda, burgers, chips, dip, mustard, ketchup, relish, etc.

It's the same with planning a report.

You set your notes into categories and list the details that fit under each category. Then you transform your plan into paragraphs.

Try making a master plan using the notes on **microwaves** listed below.

Definition	Function	Uses
A. can't be seen by human eye	A. spin water molecules within food—2.4 billion times per second	A. originally for radar
B. generated by a "magnetron"	B. vibration of molecules causes friction	B. cooking food
	C. friction causes heat	C. burning out cancer tumors
		1. tumors can't heal—then "die"

I. _____

_____

_____

II. _____

_____

_____

_____

_____

III. _____

_____

_____

_____

_____

Name _____ Date _____

Make Another Plan

Take the information from the notes below on the subject of Washington State and write a **master plan**. Remember, organizing this information gives you a chance to see what your report will look like.

Washington State

Climate
1. wet/rainy winters on west coast
2. cool/snowy autumns in foothills
3. hot/dry summers in eastern plains

Natural Resources

1. Big mountains like Mt. Rainier
   a. mountain climbing/sightseeing
   b. drinking water from snowfall
2. Columbia River runs 1,200 miles
   a. most hydroelectric power in U.S.
3. Excellent ocean harbors
4. Giant forests
5. Parks—3 national parks; 12 state parks—& historical sites

Economy

1. manufacturing
   a. aircraft—Boeing Aircraft employs 60,000
   b. computer software—500 software companies
2. farming (fruit & grains), logging, fishing
3. industry—mining
4. $66 billion in foreign trade (Japan mostly)

1. _____
   A. _____
   B. _____
   C. _____

II. _____
   A. _____
      1. _____
      2. _____
   B. _____
      1. _____
   C. _____
   D. _____
   E. _____

(continued)

Make Another Plan *(continued)*

III. _____

    A. _____

        1. _____

        2. _____

    B. _____

    C. _____

    D. _____

CHAPTER 4:

WRITING THE REPORT

Section 1: Writing the Lead

Back to Basics

Once you have a master plan, you're ready to write—to transform your plan into a report.

But exactly how do you do this?

There are several steps.
First you must build a .... **LEAD**
and write an .... **INTRODUCTION.**
Then you must use .... **TRANSITIONS,** between paragraphs.
Then you need .... **QUOTES** to make the report interesting.
And you should .... **SUMMARIZE** where necessary
and .... **PARAPHRASE.**
You must always ..... **CREDIT** information borrowed from other sources.
Finally you have to write a .... **CONCLUSION.**
Then make a .... **BIBLIOGRAPHY.**
Last, publish your report.

These skills are essential to a good report.

Practice them on the following pages before attempting a full-scale writing project.

Name _____ Date _____

Lead On!

What's a **lead**? (Pronounced "leed.")

A **lead** is an appetizer—a sentence specially made to excite the reader's appetite for more of your excellent homemade words.

Example: Which of the following two sentences is more interesting?

    a. Jane Elton thought a job on the subway would be interesting; it turned out to be the worst nightmare of her life.

    b. Subways are not as safe as they once were.

If you chose sentence b, you should probably lie down. You are not well.

Sentence a instantly hooks the reader.

> What happened to Jane?
> When did it happen?
> What were the effects on Jane?
> Is this a common occurrence?
> How can it be prevented?

Leads are up front in a report.

They lead the way into the facts and figures and quotes and percentages that are to come.

They are the first sentences the reader sees.

Three of the best types of leads are:

    QUESTION lead

    STORY lead

    QUOTE lead

Name _____ Date _____

Choose a Lead

You can start a report any way you like, but the best way to begin is with one of the three best leads in the business—the **question** lead,

the **story** lead,

or the **quote** lead.

Example: (**Question lead**) Is there one thing in life that everyone wants, that the richest person would pay anything to get? You bet there is!

(**Story lead**) Ben would go out every morning and watch the sunrise. It was peaceful. He could think things out. But today, no matter how hard he thought, no matter what possibilities he came up with, there was no true answer. His herd would have to be destroyed. That's what the inspector had said—the whole herd. Their milk was contaminated. It had been a mistake at the feed mill, and now Ben's life and future were on the line.

(**Quote lead**) "None of us expected it. We thought when we built these desktop computers that maybe the military would use them, or scientists in laboratories somewhere. We never dreamed every school kid in America would end up owning one," said Michael Horowitz, the designer of the popular Loop-De-Loop computer from Pillow Tech.

The **question lead** asks a question that makes the reader curious. The reader wants to know the answer, so he or she reads on, and on, and on.

The **story lead** introduces the reader to a character in a situation, just like in a book or on a TV program. What happens to that character becomes very important.

The **quote lead** makes the reader "listen up." The reader hears a voice. Someone is speaking. So the reader "listens," then reads on to find out the details.

What's What?

Below are 10 leads that could be used for reports. On the line before each one, indicate whether the lead is a question lead (**Qn**) a quote lead (**Qt**), or a story lead (**S**).

Example: __*Qt*__ "A hurricane is nature's way of saying, 'I am in control.' "

1. _____ "This is the greatest river on the planet. Nowhere else is life so abundant and so possible."

2. _____ By noon Jabal had sold all the birds he had captured that morning. He had worked six days, far back in the jungle; he had risked his life—all for six dollars in American money.

3. _____ With the world facing a pollution crisis the likes of which have never been seen before, what can the average teenager do?

4. _____ Rashin pedaled his bike through the streets with the skill of a dancer on a crowded stage. He dodged the woman in the yellow sari, the beggar on the corner, and the weaver at his stall in the market. Rashin was racing for home, which for him was a six-foot-by-nine-foot cardboard box on the streets of Calcutta.

5. _____ "Boarding schools are hard at first for most kids, but eventually they get used to being away from home and family and make a life of their own."

6. _____ Where can wild animals of the African plain find food, water, and rest from their enemies? In the crater of an old volcano that erupted millions of years ago and left a rich supply of food and water.

7. _____ When will the next earthquake strike California?

8. _____ What hobby requires an investment of $1.25 and provides a lifetime of satisfaction along with the potential for making a million dollars? Writing, that's what!

9. _____ "Poor children in our cities are having as tough a time getting the proper food, housing, and personal care as any poor person in the world."

10. _____ Alice loves soccer and dreams of going pro, but she will never be able to realize her dream.

X It

Reports get read when they have good leads.

Put an **X** by the five leads below that are the most interesting.

1. _____ Although many ghost towns have been demolished for highways or have deteriorated into dust, a few remain.

2. _____ The wind moaned through the empty halls of the old hotel. It slapped at the ancient wallpaper that hung in long wide curls to the floor. It blew dust in swirls across the dance hall where years before couples swayed to the music of a violin quartet. Now only the ghosts danced. The town seemed haunted and alone—just the wind and silence and dust.

3. _____ Andrew Jackson, America's seventh president, was born in the town of Waxhaw, South Carolina, on March 15, 1767, and died 78 years later on June 8, 1845.

4. _____ Which American president was captured by the British at age 13, thrown into a Revolutionary War prison, then released soon afterward to die of the smallpox he had contracted while behind bars?

5. _____ "I think the science of weather forecasting is very, very exciting."

6. _____ "If I could accurately predict the weather I'd be a ruler of kings, a legend, and a very wealthy woman."

7. _____ Imagine you are Alice, stepping through the looking glass. Suddenly everything is reversed. Doorknobs are on the wrong side of doors. The gearshift in your car is in the wrong place. Handles on can openers are on the wrong side and turn the wrong way. (Lowell Ponte, "What's Right About Being Left-Handed," *Reader's Digest*, July 1988, p. 133)

8. _____ How big is the world? You've got to answer that question if you're going to think about the environment. Is it so big that we don't have to worry about ever polluting it with our waste?

(*Science World*, "Blueprint for a Greener Planet," February 23, 1990, p. 3A)

Name _____   Date _____

New, Improved Leads

The two leads below are dull, dead, and discouraging. Rewrite them using more details—a few adjectives and adverbs, an interesting verb or two, combined with a fresh perspective on the subject.

Example: **(Dull Lead)**
Mousetraps are used to catch mice, and a lot of people use these devices to get rid of mice in their basements and attics.

(Improved Version)
Murder is a nasty word. We shudder at the thought of anyone who could do such a terrible thing. But when it comes to killing mice, even the kindest person can turn into a cold-hearted executioner.

1. "I believe seeing-eye dogs are very interesting dogs."

   (Use a quote lead.) _____

   _____

   _____

   _____

2. Is it really all that great being a beauty queen?

   (Use a qestion lead.) _____

   _____

   _____

   _____

More Improved Leads

Use your creative skills to put some new life into the leads below. Make them interesting and informative.

1. "A lot of teens spend a lot of hours in front of the television."

   (Quote lead) _____

   _____

   _____

   _____

   _____

2. When Christmas comes, do you spend a lot of money?

   (Question lead) _____

   _____

   _____

   _____

   _____

3. Jim walked out to his girlfriend's car and drove away with it.

   (Story lead) _____

   _____

   _____

   _____

   _____

   _____

Do All Three

Using the sentence below about smoking and chewing tobacco, create three different leads—one quote lead, one question lead, one story lead—that could be used to begin three different reports.

Sentence: MANY PEOPLE, EVEN THOUGH THEY KNOW IT'S UNHEALTHY, STILL SMOKE AND CHEW TOBACCO.

1. (Quote lead) _____

_____

_____

_____

2. (Question lead) _____

_____

_____

_____

_____

_____

3. (Story lead) _____

_____

_____

_____

_____

_____

_____

Section 2: Writing Introductions

Name _____ Date _____

Making Introductions

What happens after the lead?

You can't start in with facts and figures and quotes and percentages because no one really knows where you're headed. It would be like throwing the reader into a cold swimming pool—shocking!

For example, let's say your story lead was this:

When Jean got to the scene of the accident, the boy was already dead. His mother, who was in shock, lay pinned under the car. The only thing to do was cut the car apart. Jean went to the back of the truck, got the saw, and ran back to the wreck. But then she stopped. As she bent over the crushed hood of the car, her hands went numb. She couldn't move.

What is your report topic? . . . the effects of shock on accident victims?

     . . . the training needs of parademics?

     . . . how fear can block human actions?

     . . . the new tools used by rescue teams?

No one really knows what your topic is yet because leads simply get the reader hooked; they don't always tell exactly what the report is about.

So after your lead, you need a paragraph (three to five sentences) that introduces the topic of the report.

This is called an **introduction**, and no report would be complete without one.

How to Do It

To write good **introductions**, you work outward from your report topics to more general topics, until you get to the most general topic and begin there with your first sentence.

Here's how:

Let's say your report is about diamond rings. After your lead, you would ask, "What larger category would include diamond rings?" The answer is *jewelry.* Then you would find a broader category of which jewelry is a part, which could be *gifts*; there are many kinds of gifts, and jewelry is just one. Then you would ask, "What broad, general category would gifts come under?" The answer could be: things we give on *important occasions.* So important occasions is where you would start your introduction.

Occasions . . .

Gifts . . .

Jewelry . . .

Diamond Rings . . .

Your **introduction** might read like this:

Every year is filled with special occasions that include the giving of gifts: Christmas, Valentine's Day, birthdays, weddings, and so on. And one of the most commonly given gifts for such occasions is some type of jewelry. But just not any jewelry. For that special occasion, the moment that marks a very important event, many people choose a well-known but expensive item, the diamond ring.

Notice . . . the introduction begins with occasions, then moves to gifts, then to jewelry, then to a specific kind of jewelry, diamond rings. By gradually leading your reader to your subject, you have built some small suspense into the often tiresome process of acquiring information.

Do It Yourself

Reports can be on any subject. And any subject can be introduced in a clear three- to five-sentence paragraph.

For example, your report could be on the surrender of General Lee to General Grant at Appomattox Court House in April of 1865. Your introduction would have to start with a general subject and move to the specific event that took place: the surrender.

Here is how the progression from the general to the specific might go:

WAR . . .

CIVIL WAR . . .

MAJOR EVENTS . . .

THE SURRENDER . . .

Write an introduction using a sentence for each of the areas listed above. The first sentence is given as a guideline.

Introduction:

War is one of humankind's greatest tragedies.

_____

_____

_____

_____

_____

_____

_____

_____

Write an Introduction

Read the following **introduction**:

The world has always contained a variety of strange creatures. Centuries past, huge dinosaurs roamed the earth, while today 200-pound snakes crawl through the jungles of South America and 18-foot crocodiles slither through the swamps of Florida. But one of the strangest animals weighs only a few ounces—a mammal that flies. It sleeps during the day and flies at night, sometimes seeking blood for its nourishment. This creature is the mysterious bat.

Notice . . .   The first sentence is general, about a "variety" of creatures.

The second sentence is more specific, naming dinosaurs, snakes, and crocodiles.

The third and fourth sentences give a specific description of a particular mammal.

The fourth sentence finally names the BAT.

Try it: Write an introduction about the subject of Siamese cats. Start general and get specific.

General statement about animals.

_____

_____

_____

_____

_____

_____

_____

(continued)

Write an Introduction *(continued)*

More specific statement about using some animals as pets.

_____

_____

_____

_____

_____

_____

More specific statement about cats as pets.

_____

_____

_____

_____

Name a specific cat . . . Siamese.

_____

_____

_____

_____

_____

Name _____ Date _____

On Your Own

Write an **introduction** for a report on the famous educational television show *Sesame Street*. (Read the notes in parentheses to get suggestions for the sentences you need.)

(General statement about how education is important at an early age.)

_____

_____

_____

(More specific statement about how education at home may be as important as at school.)

_____

_____

_____

(More specific statement about using television for education.)

_____

_____

_____

(Statement that names *Sesame Street* as the oldest educational TV show.)

_____

_____

_____

Another Introduction

Write an **introduction** for a report on roller coasters.

(General statement about amusement parks)

_____

_____

_____

(Famous amusement parks)

_____

_____

_____

(Specific rides at most parks)

_____

_____

_____

(Roller coaster)

_____

_____

_____

The Great Combination

Combine the two skills you've just learned by writing a lead AND an introduction for a report on the subject of horror movies.

Use a story lead about someone in a theater getting more and more terrified. Then move on to a general statement that applies the experience of being terrified and thrilled to all of us—a sentence like this:

Being thrilled and shocked has always been a main reason for people going to the movies.

Then tell how two different kinds of movies (other than horror films) thrill us—for example, cop shows provide danger and stunts.

Then tell how horror movies especially shock us with their evil surprises.

(Story Lead)

_____

_____

_____

_____

(Introduction)

_____

_____

_____

_____

_____

_____

_____

_____

Another Great Combo

Write a **quote lead** and an **introduction** for a report on the subject of black widow spiders. You don't have to be an authority on this subject to write a lead or an introduction. Just get the reader interested with a good quote about spiders. Then introduce the subject of frightening creatures, list a few specific kinds, then mention the black widow, one of the most feared. (The body of your report will tell the rest of the details.)

(Quote Lead)

_____

_____

_____

_____

(Introduction)

_____

_____

_____

_____

_____

_____

_____

_____

_____

Name _____ Date _____

One More Combo

Write a **question lead** and an **introduction** for a report on the subject of bicycles. Hook the reader with an interesting question, then write a general statement that answers the question, followed by more and more specific statements till you get to the subject of bicycles.

Note: If you choose to use a lead in your report (some reports start with just the introduction), you may treat the lead as a separate paragraph and then indent when you begin the introduction.

(Question Lead)

_____

_____

_____

_____

_____

_____

(Introduction)

_____

_____

_____

_____

_____

_____

_____

_____

_____

Section 3: Using Transitions

Name _____ Date _____

Stayin' Alive!

In a report, the information that follows the lead and introduction is called the **body** of the report. Unfortunately, in many reports, the body is dead.

And here's the reason . . . a lot of folks can write a luring lead followed by a dazzling introduction, but few can keep the reader interested for three, four, or five pages.

Why?

Because too many writers create their own "static" or "interference" by writing their message in a confused order. They don't take the reader from the beginning through the middle to the end. Too many times readers have to stop and ask, "What?"

The key word is **order**.

Certain things have to happen at a certain time:

• You don't put your socks and shoes on and then take a shower.

• You don't butter your bread and then toast it.

• You don't get an *A* and then write a good report.

Many reports could benefit from a chronological pattern, or a "time order." Let's say you were writing about Emily Dickinson, the great New England poet. A good way to begin would be to start with her childhood, then describe her life as a teenager and young adult, explain her life-style as a middle-aged woman, then tell of her experience in the last years of her life. Finally, you could tell how her work has influenced poets right up through modern times.

That's "time order."

It's a simple, direct way to get the reader from the introduction of your report to the conclusion.

All in Order

Most reports lend themselves to "time order":

● The Rocky Mountains evolved over a long period of *time*.

● The Soo Locks were built over a period of *time*.

● The Civil War took place over a *time span* of four years.

● Mark Twain lived in the *time* between 1835 and 1910.

Almost any report can be organized around the concept of *time*—when something happened; when something was built; when to do something first, second, next, and last.

So "time words" become very important to writers, words like:

first, second, then, next, followed by, afterward, meanwhile, before, during, until, to begin with, initially, in the first place, in the second place, third, finally, last, in the end.

Historical dates are important, too:

"By *1861* the worst war in America's history . . . "

In fact, our language is full of "time words" and "time phrases."

Exercise: On the lines below, tell what happened in the last good movie you saw or in the most recent book you read. Circle the "time" words—*then, next, finally, . . .*

_____

_____

_____

_____

_____

_____

_____

_____

Order Up!

Below are 18 subjects for possible reports. Decide which ones could be written using "time order." Mark your choices with a **T**.

Example: _____ underwater caves

         __T__ the life of Ida Tarbell

         _____ barbells

1. _____ kangaroos

2. _____ how the Pilgrims got to America

3. _____ the development of the "Big Mac" burger

4. _____ the history of Little League baseball

5. _____ how to collect baseball cards

6. _____ the life of Jane Addams

7. _____ the biography of Betsy Ross

8. _____ how fish are canned

9. _____ the history of Montreal

10. _____ the assassination of President Lincoln

11. _____ how to put on a play

12. _____ the top ten Christmas gifts

13. _____ how to become a lifeguard

14. _____ the life and times of the brontosaurus

15. _____ the Ice Age

16. _____ dandelions

17. _____ Alfred Nobel and the Nobel Prize

18. _____ the life of Harriet Tubman

Name _____   Date _____

Find the Time

Read the paragraphs below and circle all the "time words" that help connect the ideas and make the sentences flow together.

1. Washing the family car is a step-by-step process. You first must select a proper site—parking the car too near the neighbor will result in your washing the side of his house as well as your mom's van. Second, a hose long enough to reach the van would be helpful; vehicles washed from long distance never get sparkling clean. Next, you need to gather two buckets of warm water, one for the body of the vehicle and one for the muddy bumpers and wheels. Then you should spray the entire car before applying soap and sponge. And finally, be sure to park the vehicle out of the hot sun so the soap doesn't bake on before you can hose it off.

2. Writing a report requires a lot more than summarizing an article out of an encyclopedia. To begin, you need a topic—not just any topic, but something you're interested in and maybe know a little about. Then you must find sources for information about your subject. You can interview people, watch videos, read articles, listen to cassettes, or read research texts and books on the subject. After you find and read sources, you must take notes, organize them into an outline, and write the rough draft of your report. (Be sure to include quotes from experts and all recent information, and credit that information.) Following the writing of the rough draft, you must revise and edit your work to create a publishable report, something you can proudly turn in as a piece of your best work.

All in Due Time

The sentences in the paragraphs below are jumbled. They need to be organized. Decide which sentence should come first and mark it #1, then mark the sentence that should come next #2, mark the next sentence #3, and so on.

PARAGRAPH A

_____ To be an effective bird-watcher, you must first buy good binoculars, boots, and a notebook.

_____ Then you must find a place where birds spend time.

_____ Finally, if you find something unusual, you can report your findings to the local Sapsucker Club or some other bird-watching organization in your area.

_____ Once you find a good watching place, you must carefully record your observations.

PARAGRAPH B

_____ By 1607 America had its first hotel, the Jamestown Inn, in Jamestown, Virginia.

_____ These early Greek hotels were called inns and were situated along roads and trails where people traveled with their goods to market.

_____ About A.D. 900 an inn called the Hospice of St. Bernard was built in Italy by monks; it housed 300 people and kept large dogs that were used to find travelers lost in the mountains.

_____ Though the world has come to see hotels as modern conveniences, they were in existence as early as 500 B.C., in Greece.

_____ Since then Americans have built thousands of small hotels called "motels" located along almost every main road in almost every town in the United States.

(Albert Kudrle, "Hotels and Motels," *The New Book of Knowledge,* Grolier Inc., 1982, pp. 256–59)

Name _____ Date _____

Fill in the Time

Below are two paragraphs whose "time connectors" are missing. Using some of the samples from the box, fill in the blanks with the words that make the smoothest transitions between sentences.

Samples: *first, second, third, then, next, after, following this, to begin, meanwhile, once that's done, eventually, initially, since, finally*

PARAGRAPH #1

Moving to a new place is a process filled with high hopes and high anxiety, but it can be done well if a few careful steps are taken. _____ when you move, it is best to learn all the information available about the place to which you're headed. The fewer surprises, the better. _____ you'll want to check out the quality of moving companies, and the best source for this is friends and neighbors who have moved themselves; ask how the moving company treated them and their belongings. _____ you'll need to plan the actual journey—will you follow the moving truck or go on ahead and make final preparations for the new house or apartment? _____ , when you're moved in to the new place, you'll need to find ways to meet your neighbors and make friends. Being the newcomer on the block, you'll need all the support you can get.

PARAGRAPH #2

One of the most important things we do is communicate, and to help us do this we have no better friend than the mail service. It began about 4,000 years ago when people first wrote messages on clay tablets and messengers delivered them on foot. _____ about 2400 B.C. papyrus, a type of paper, was developed by the Egyptians, which made transporting letters and legal documents a lot easier. By 1533 King Henry VIII had established private mail service for citizens. His example was _____ carried over to the United States. Ships used to carry mail across the Atlantic from England to the colonies. By 1830 America's mail was carried by train, until air travel surpassed the speed of even the fastest locomotive. _____ the 1950's America has relied most heavily on air mail for efficient postal service.

Name _____ Date _____

Write It!

Try your skill using time transitions by writing two paragraphs on the lines below. Remember, not every sentence needs a time transition—two or three per paragraph will get the job done.

PARAGRAPH #1

Tell the reader exactly how to go about doing something like saddling a horse, catching a lobster, or cleaning a dirty bedroom.

_____

_____

_____

_____

_____

_____

PARAGRAPH #2

Explain how something works—how a toaster toasts, or how a blender blends, or how a dumpling dumples (just kidding).

_____

_____

_____

_____

_____

_____

On the Move

Humans are always on the move, going places, seeing things. Even when we're asleep our bodies are moving—our hearts are pumping, blood is traveling to every cell in our bodies, and our lungs are rising and falling as we breathe.

With all this movement within us it is no surprise that our talk and our writing are full of movement too. When we describe something, we move our eyes along an object and describe it from left to right or top to bottom. We might explain the structure of a volcano by starting from the inside and working to the outside. We could report on how a pyramid is built from the ground up.

This is called **spatial order** because we are telling about things in terms of *where* they are.

The screen, or monitor, sits *above* the computer and shows every word, line, or circle made at the keyboard. *Beneath* the screen is the stand upon which the screen rests. The stand sits firmly *on* the computer body or on a shelf just *above* the computer.

In this example, words like *above, beneath,* and *on* are used to guide our eyes down along the computer in an orderly, logical manner.

This is **spatial** order.

Lewis Thomas, in his book *Lives of a Cell*, described the earth from 240,000 miles away, looking from outside our atmosphere in toward our planet.

Viewed *from the distance* of the moon, the astonishing thing about the earth, catching the breath, is that it is alive. The photographs show the dry, pounded surface of the moon in the *foreground*, dead as an old bone. Aloft, floating free *beneath* the moist, gleaming membrane of bright blue sky, is the rising earth, the only exuberant thing in this part of the cosmos.

This is **spatial** order used to its outer limits.

Space Language

Have you ever watched a home movie or video where the camera person must have just walked off a roller coaster? People appear, then disappear. Rooms come into view, then vanish. The camera starts on the left of a room, then jumps to the right, then up to the ceiling, then down to the floor, then back to the left where the kids are perched on the sofa.

That kind of viewing can give you a headache that a pill can't reach.

And the same thing can happen with writing. An author can pull you all over a building or a place or an object till you're dizzy. Your mind's eye has no pattern to follow. There's no easy movement along an object or across a subject. It's frustrating, and few reports like this are ever read completely.

The language of space can help in these situations. If a writer wants to describe an object or tell how something is constructed, he or she can choose from a long list of **space** words like these:

above	between	within
across	beyond	in front
against	up	in back
along	down	outside
amidst	under	inside
around	on top	left
behind	near	right
beside	over	on bottom
beneath	past	inward
below	upon	outward

Name _____   Date _____

Space Words in Action

The box below contains words often used to show **spatial** order.

Use some of these words to describe the ice cream sundae of your wildest dreams. Begin at the top of the sundae and work down. Go ahead—make me drool!

at the top	underneath	beside
beneath	within	around
below	under	at the bottom

_____

_____

_____

_____

_____

_____

_____

_____

Now, list the space words (transitions) you used.

_____

_____

_____

Name _____ Date _____

Time or Space

Below is a combined list of "time" transitions and "space" transitions. Put a **T** next to each time transition, and put an **S** by each space transition.

Example: __T__ first
__S__ near

1. _____ second

2. _____ third

3. _____ right

4. _____ left

5. _____ up

6. _____ upon

7. _____ within

8. _____ eventually

9. _____ meanwhile

10. _____ underneath

11. _____ afterward

12. _____ below

13. _____ finally

14. _____ then

15. _____ inside

16. _____ above

17. _____ adjoining

18. _____ alongside

19. _____ beyond

20. _____ around

21. _____ last

22. _____ simultaneously

23. _____ east

24. _____ later

25. _____ beside

26. _____ beneath

27. _____ under

28. _____ following that

29. _____ to begin with

30. _____ in front

31. _____ in back

32. _____ bottom

33. _____ over

34. _____ across

35. _____ next

136

Going in Circles

Read the two paragraphs below, then circle the spatial transitions. Remember, transitions can be one word or a group of words like "By the door . . . " or "Next to the supercharger. . . ."

PARAGRAPH #1

A volcano begins deep below the earth's surface where molten rock and hot gases form in pools. The rock is called magma, and when the pressure from the gases builds high enough, the magma is shot upward along a main channel, called a center vent, that runs through the middle of the volcano. The magma (called lava when it hits the surface) pours out into the crater formed at the very top of the volcano, then builds into a lake of fiery rock which spills over the sides of the bowl-shaped crater and runs down the outer wall of the volcano onto the land. When it cools and hardens, the crater is a vast bowl with high sides and a deep center. As years pass and the volcano dies out, the creater can become an important place for people and animals. In Africa, old volcano craters serve as excellent sources of grass and water for elephants, lions, and other big game.

PARAGRAPH #2

A pop-top can is an interesting bit of engineering and design. At the top lies a tab of aluminum that's riveted to the surface of the can. Below the tab is a circular indentation that is scribed so that it is weaker than the surrounding metal. When the tab is pulled up, the rivet acts as a hinge and the nose of the tab forces the precut circle to give way. A neat round hole is made through which soda can flow. The top surface is flat and rimmed in a circle with a ⅛″ ridge of aluminum which keeps the can from being crushed during shipping, and which also catches some of the liquid when the can is jostled. Below the rim, the can tapers out slightly, then follows straight down to where a final taper inward creates a base slightly smaller in diameter than the top; this allows the can to be easily stacked on other cans in a shipping case. The sides are flexible yet strong and in a round shape that fits the hand well. With a quick tug, you can pop the top of such a can and tip the cool soda down your thirsty throat.

Name _____ Date _____

Your Own Space

Using two of the topics listed below, or two of your own, write two paragraphs that use spatial transitions to explain the structure of an object. Remember, *not* every sentence needs a transition—two or three per paragraph will be enough.

- The structure of the planet Saturn
- A description of a soccer field
- A description of a running shoe
- The design of a 10-speed bike
- The interior of a rocket's command module

1. _____

_____

_____

_____

_____

_____

_____

_____

_____

2. _____

_____

_____

_____

_____

_____

_____

_____

_____

A Great Combo

One of the greatest combinations in the world is not a hamburger and fries, it's the space-time combo.

Every report, if it's to be interesting, uses a variety of methods to get its message across. And the best method is actually a combination of two methods—**time order** and **spatial order**.

Example: If you were to write a report about the Great Wall of China, the only human-made structure seen from the moon, you could begin the body of your report with facts about *when* different portions of the Great Wall were built—who was emperor at the time, who was at war with whom, what was happening in other countries around the world during different phases of the Wall's construction.

In another section of your report you could tell about *where* the Great Wall goes on its 1,500-mile journey across China—the provinces, the people who live in certain areas, the geography of different parts of China.

Then you could talk about the actual *structure* of the Wall—its shape, size, and design (guard towers, walkways, height and thickness of the wall, etc.).

The combination of time order and spatial order would make any report, even a biography, more complete.

A report on Harriet Tubman, for example, could include:

(**time**)—   when she was born,

when she escaped from slavery,

when she began freeing slaves.

(**space**)—   a description of her from head to toe,

a description of where the "underground railroad" traveled,

a description of the states in the South where Harriet traveled.

Name _____ Date _____

Time-Space Report

Using both spatial and chronological (time) transitions, write a mini-report about Santa Claus. First describe this legendary, generous character using **spatial** transitions. Then write a paragraph about the history of the Santa Claus legend using **time transitions** and the information listed below taken from *The World Book Encyclopedia,* 1976, Volume 17, pp. 101–102.

- A.D. 300's, the real Saint Nicholas lived in Myra, a town in Turkey.

- 6th century A.D., Saint Nicholas became the patron saint of schoolboys.

- Middle Ages, Saint Nicholas was shown as a hairy little elf in Germany.

- In 1809 in America, Washington Irving described Saint Nicholas as a jolly fellow who smoked a pipe.

- In 1822 Clement Moore wrote "The Night Before Christmas," in which Saint Nicholas was a jolly, old, fat, white-whiskered elf.

_____

_____

_____

_____

_____

_____

_____

_____

_____

_____

_____

_____

_____

_____

Time and Space Together

Using the historical information listed below and a description of any modern coin, write two paragraphs for a report about coins. Use the back of this sheet or another piece of paper if you need more room.

- First metal coins were small bronze models of hoes, knives, and keys made by the Chinese about 1100 B.C.

- Gold and silver coins were made by the Lydians about 700 B.C.

- Aegean people used pure silver in coins called "turtles" about 625 B.C.

- Pure gold was used by King Croesus in 560 B.C.

- King Philip of Macedon issued first copper coins about 39 B.C.

(Source: Sam Rosenfeld, *The Story of Coins*, Harvey House Publishers, NY 1968)

_____

_____

_____

_____

_____

_____

_____

One of the most interesting coins minted today is . . . _____

_____

_____

_____

_____

_____

_____

Section 4: Summarizing

Name _____ Date _____

Two Key Skills

A report is more than a bunch of credits behind bits of information borrowed from a bunch of books.

A good report brings together different perspectives on a subject and puts them into one document. A report must be based on many different sources, so a variety of viewpoints and different kinds of information are presented.

Example: If you were to write a report on the great fire of 1988 in Yellowstone National Park, it would be wise to get information from the National Park Service because its people were on the scene. But it would also be wise to get information from people who lived nearby and from people who often travel to the park for recreation and sightseeing. And it would be smart to read articles in newspapers like *The New York Times,* whose reporters don't live in or near Yellowstone Park. And of course, it would be great if you could go there yourself to see the damage and report your observations.

This kind of report-writing takes more than a bunch of facts and figures. It takes understanding. To help you understand a subject, you can use two key report-writing skills: **summarizing** and **paraphrasing**.

With these skills you can get to the core of an article and understand what it's really saying. Without these skills you can read a dozen books and still not be able to sit down and put all the information into a solid, interesting, intelligent report.

Summarizing

When you add numbers you get a sum, a total.

When you add words, the same thing can happen.

Example: What can you "sum up" from the following sentences?

1. It is 7:50 A.M. when your alarm clock starts "singing."
2. School starts at 8:00.
3. It takes 20 minutes to get ready.
4. It takes 20 minutes to walk to school.

Summary = YOU'RE GOING TO BE LATE!

The word *summary* comes from the word *sum*, which means "total."

Skip the details.
Skip the adjectives.
Get to the point.
Summarize!

Summarizing is the skill of getting to the core of a sentence, or a paragraph, or an entire book.

Summarizing gives a one-sentence "sum total" of the meaning of a piece of written or spoken communication.

Summarizing is like skipping the sucker and getting right to the chocolate inside!

Find the "Sum Totals"

Write a one-sentence summary that draws a conclusion from the sentences in groups A, B, and C below.

Group A: 1. Your parents do not want you going to the park after dark alone.

2. It's dark outside.

3. You go to the park with a friend.

4. Your parents don't know your friend is with you.

_____

Conclusion Summary = "   "

Group B: 1. The bus leaves school at 3:30.

2. Play tryouts will last till 5:30.

3. You are trying out for the play.

4. Your parents want you to call them if you ever need a ride home.

_____

Conclusion Summary = "   "

Group C: 1. You enjoy farm life and working with animals.

2. You do not like the crowds and the noise of the city.

3. You have a chance to work in your uncle's restaurant downtown.

4. You have an offer to work part-time at your grandma's farm for the summer.

5. You definitely want to work to make extra spending money.

_____

Conclusion Summary = "   "

Get to the Point

All summaries aren't conclusions.

Some summaries are just shortened versions of a long message, like writing a telegram instead of a letter.

For example;

Letter: Dear Mom,

   The semester is over and I'm glad to be coming home. I will be flying in on Tuesday and should get home about 9 P.M. Tuesday night. Of course, if there are any flight delays I'll call so you won't worry. See you soon.

                                    Love,

                                    Marlene

Telegram: Arriving Tuesday 9 P.M.

   Will call if delayed.

               Marlene

On the lines provided, write a telegram for the following letter:

Dear Dad,

   I know you and Mom spent a lot of money to send me here to soccer camp, but it's just not working out. I don't seem to fit in with the kids and it's boring most of the time. I'd rather kick the ball around with you like we've always done. If it's not too much trouble, could you come and get me this Saturday? I'll be at the main office by 8 o'clock in the morning with my bags packed.

Love,

Roger

Telegram: _____

_____

_____

More Summaries

Anyone can summarize anything.

Take books, for example. You can tell in one sentence what the book *The Black Stallion* is about by saying:

> "It's the story of a boy who saves the life of an Arabian stallion who then becomes the boy's true friend forever."

You can summarize a movie the same way.

Take *E.T.*, for example. You could say:

> "It's about an alien who gets left behind and who makes friends with an earth boy who then helps the lovable creature escape nosy scientists and return home."

You could summarize a fairy tale like Cinderella:

> "It's about a mistreated girl who becomes a princess in an instant because she has the right shoe size."

EXERCISE

Write a summary for the classics listed below.

The Wizard of Oz

_____

_____

Treasure Island

_____

_____

Rudolph the Red-Nosed Reindeer

_____

_____

Get Serious

Summaries can also be a serious help when you are researching different sources for a report.

Example: Let's say you want to do a report on how conserving energy can help preserve the environment. In your research you read the following paragraph:

> Americans are wasting energy in many different ways. One third of the heat lost in a home goes out through the cracks in and around closed windows, even though there are ways available to cut that loss by 90 percent. Also, appliances use more energy than they need to; refrigerators use about 7 percent of the electricity in the average home, and though energy-efficient models exist, they are more expensive and people won't buy them. Lighting, too, takes a lot of energy—25 percent of the electricity used in a home. But again, efficient lighting devices cost more, and people won't purchase them."

(Based on an article by David Fisher in *Health,* Jan. 1990, p. 31)

You wouldn't copy this paragraph word for word because that's a waste of energy—too much time! And you might not want all those little percentages because you may already have details from other sources.

So you SUMMARIZE: "Americans waste energy through leaky windows, appliances, and lighting."

That's it.

That's a SUMMARY of the paragraph on energy loss.

You could combine this summary with summaries from other books and articles about energy waste and come up with an interesting paragraph. In fact, that's how most paragraphs in most reports are written.

Name _____   Date _____

The Summary Syndrome

Write a summary for each of the paragraphs below. (You won't need the details, which is good, because they were invented for this exercise and are totally inaccurate.)

The travel industry wastes a tremendous amount of energy every day of every year due to poor combustion of fossil fuels like diesel fuel and gasoline. Every day, 50 million gallons of fuel are consumed by buses whose routes cover thousands of miles from coast to coast. This produces 5 million tons of carbon waste products every 24 hours. Train travel, the most economical means of transporting anything over long distances, pours 100,000 tons of carbon dioxide into the air each day. But there's more. The airline industry logs hundreds of millions of miles a year and blackens the skies with its tonnage of pollutants. This waste of fuel due to inefficient combustion, coupled with the cost of cleaning up the environment, results in the greatest waste of energy this world has ever seen.

America's love affair with cars has caused a lot of problems for the earth's atmosphere. Two billion tons of carbon dioxide an hour are being pumped into the air from cars and trucks on America's highways. Scientists are alarmed. This kind of waste can foul the air in countries as distant as China and Australia. To keep these cars running, 500,000 barrels of oil an hour are pumped into the tanks of waiting motorists At this pace, the United States could be in a serious oil/energy shortage within 10 brief years. And cars aren't the only culprits. With 202 million lawn mowers, garden tillers, and chain saws, weekend cleanups cost the environment dearly. And let us not forget America's addiction to motorized recreation: motorcycles, mini-bikes, powerboats, motor homes, four-wheelers, and snowmobiles. Fifty thousand gallons of oil are consumed each hour each weekend by people who just want to have fun.

Summaries

Paragraph 1. _____

_____

_____

_____

_____

_____

Paragraph 2. _____

_____

_____

_____

_____

Name _____ Date _____

The 1-2-3 Combination

The bulk of the information in a report is not facts, figures, and percentages. It's general summaries collected from several different sources on a certain subject.

For example, the three summary statements from the previous two pages dealing with the use and waste of energy in the United States could be combined to make a good summary paragraph.

Here's how:

Sentence 1:   "Americans waste energy through leaky windows, appliances, and lighting."

Sentence 2:   "Buses, trains, and aircraft pump millions of tons of pollutants into the earth's atmosphere while consuming millions of gallons of the world's oil supply."

Sentence 3:   "Other contributors to America's energy waste are cars and tools (like chain saws and lawn mowers) and recreational machines (like motorcycles and power boats.)"

Now COMBINE these sentences into a summary paragraph:

"Americans waste energy in a number of ways. <u>First,</u> homeowners waste energy by letting heat escape through cracks around windows, and by using inefficient appliances and lights. <u>Then</u> all the machines we use to take us places, like buses, trains, and airplanes, consume large amounts of fuel and pump tons of pollutants into the atmosphere each day. <u>And to top it off,</u> America's cars and recreational vehicles like motorcycles and powerboats consume a large amount of the world's oil supply while polluting the air we breathe."

Notice the connecting words that are underlined. Also, look at the topic sentence used. Both of these "tools" help the summary paragraph make sense.

Be a "Summary" Warrior

Read the three paragraphs below and write a summary sentence for each one. Then combine the sentences into a summary paragraph.

The 4.6-billion-year history of the planet is one of unceasing subterranean turmoil that produces more than a million tremors each year—an average of one every 30 seconds. The vast majority of these quakes are scarcely strong enough to rattle a teacup in its saucer, but more than 3,000 a year move the surface noticeably. Hundreds produce significant changes in the face of the land. More than 20 each year cause severe distortions—and when they strike heavily populated areas they are catastrophic.

The human toll in these major quakes can be appalling. Earthquakes and their resultant tsunamis, fires, plagues, and deprivations today claim an average of 10,000 to 15,000 lives every year. The figures are even more staggering in historical perspective: The number of people known to have died from the sudden quaking of the earth has exceeded 13 million since written records have been kept.

No place or time is entirely safe. Though spared the fearsome frequency with which earthquakes strike some parts of the globe, the African highlands, the steppes of Asia, the Amazon rain forest, and the American plains and Eastern Seaboard have all been visited by the horror of heaving earth and crumbling buildings. In the year following the great Alaska quake of 1964, 22 major earthquakes occurred around the world. The year was far from extraordinary for its seismic activity. This is the way it has always been. (Based on *Earthquakes* (Planet Earth Series), by Bryce S. Walker, Time-Life Books, 1982, p. 43)

Summary sentence, paragraph 1: _____

_____

Summary sentence, paragraph 2: _____

_____

Summary sentence, paragraph 3: _____

_____

Summary paragraph: _____

_____

_____

_____

_____

_____

_____

_____

Combination II

Write a summary sentence for each paragraph below. Then combine sentences into a summary paragraph. (Use a topic sentence and a few connectors like *also,* and *furthermore.*)

The great Yellowstone fire of 1988 started on June 23 when a bolt of lightning struck the dry forest near the southern end of the park. A light snow pack and little rain had left the land as dry as paper. Once the fire started, the Park Service decided to let it burn in order to clear out much of the dead and fallen trees and underbrush. The high winds kicked up and spread the fire through stretches of forest that held no roads or other breaks where the fire might halt.

Quickly people realized the fire could not be "let go," and 4,400 army troops were flown in to fight the flames. By September, 9,500 people were engaged in the battle. Air tankers and helicopters, 117 of them, were used to drop water and fire-retardant chemicals. Mules hauled supplies into camps in the back country where fire-fighters were stationed. When the fire spread outside the park, local village fire departments raced to save lives and property.

A lot was lost in the tragic blaze. Supplies, equipment, and people to fight the fire cost $3 million a day. The fire destroyed 3 homes; 13 mobile homes, 31 cabins, and 243 elk also perished in the flames. Workers hauled 10 million gallons of water to dump on the fire along with 1.4 million gallons of fire retardant. In all, 18,000 hours of flying time were logged in the 4-month struggle to get the inferno under control. (Based on: *Yellowstone on Fire,* by *Billings Gazette* reporters, Falcon Press, Helena, MT, 1989).

Summary sentence, paragraph 1: _____

_____

Summary sentence, paragraph 2: _____

_____

_____

Summary sentence, paragraph 3: _____

_____

_____

Summary paragraph: _____

_____

_____

_____

_____

_____

Section 5: Paraphrasing

Name _____ Date _____

Your Own Style

Summaries are like tossed salads—sometimes they're just not enough.

If you're researching the subject of volcanoes, for example, and you find a paragraph in a text that's so full of solid information that you want to use the whole thing in your report, how can you do it?

You can't copy it word for word because that's **plagiarism**—word stealing.

You can't summarize the paragraph because a summary is too brief.

So what do you do?

You can **paraphrase,** that's what.

Here's how:

1. Read the paragraph carefully, concentrating on its basic meaning and content.
2. Try to picture yourself repeating the contents of the paragraph to a stranger, someone who knows nothing about the subject.
3. Write down that conversation you had in your mind using your own words and expressions to get the meaning across.

That's it.

You've paraphrased.

If you can learn to **paraphrase,** you will find that writing reports is not so much a look-it-up-and-copy exercise as it is practice in thinking about how to express new facts and ideas in your own personal style.

Don't Plagiarize

Some people act like human photocopy machines. They copy, copy, copy. When they're done, they turn in their "work" as a finished report.

This is called word-stealing, or **plagiarism.** It is a serious offense. You can go to court for stealing someone's words or ideas.

A way to avoid plagiarism is to **paraphrase.** You can write your own version of an article using your own words and personal style and still keep the meaning of the original article or book you researched. You need only to list the source of your information on the "Works Consulted" page, which we will discuss later.

Read the paragraph below taken from *Volcano,* (Planet Earth Series), by the editors of Time-Life Books, 1982.

> The eruptions of volcanoes are the source of the primeval and continuing regeneration of mountains and plains. The ocean floor, science now knows, is the result of millions of years of slow but ceaseless volcanic extrusions emanating from a 30,000-mile-long chain of deep-sea rift valleys. A volcano's noxious ash and gases are essential to life on earth. The billions of tons of mineral-rich ash that fall to earth after an eruption are transformed in time into the most fertile of soils. Volcanologists calculate that, judging by their present rate of activity, volcanoes could have accounted for nearly a quarter of the oxygen, hydrogen, carbon, chlorine, and nitrogen in the biosphere and may, in fact, have been the primal source for most of the earth's air and water.

Now read the **paraphrased** version.

When the earth was young, volcanoes played a major role in forming the land we walk on and the air we breathe. Volcanoes helped form mountains; they formed rich topsoil by blowing tons of nutrients and minerals into the air that settled to earth. In fact, the ocean floor itself was formed by volcanoes erupting along a 30,000-mile stretch of deep-sea valleys. And finally, the very air we breathe could have come from early volcanic explosions that threw huge amounts of nitrogen, oxygen, carbon, hydrogen, and chlorine into the biosphere.

A **paraphrase** is a writer's own words on a particular subject.

Para-Steps

The actual steps required to write a good paraphrase are simple.

Step 1: Decode the vocabulary. Take all the "big" words and run them through a dictionary—look them up. Then find a shorter, simpler, more direct word that means the same thing:

big instead of *gargantuan*

slow instead of *plodding*

Step 2: Eliminate all the flowery adverbs and adjectives like:

unusually

somewhat

rather

extensive

sensational

laborious

Step 3: Eliminate quotes from experts, and avoid percentages and facts that you don't need to get the main meaning across. The only time you would need to paraphrase a quote is if it is very important, or if it is extremely long (three to ten lines) and you want to shorten it so you can get on with your message.

Step 4: After figuring out the vocabulary and eliminating flowery adjectives and adverbs and quotes that don't say much, pull out just the important sentences in the paragraph, combine some of them using *and,* shorten others, then add a few of your own adjectives, and write an original paraphrase. HINT: By starting your paraphrase with the last piece of information in the original paragraph, you can give your version a different look and a touch more originality.

Para-Practice I

The steps involved in paraphrasing can be applied to any paragraph, like the one below on child abduction. Examine carefully how the four steps to paraphrasing are applied. You can write a good paraphrase of almost anything if you know exactly how to do it.

Although kidnappings attract intense media attention, they are actually quite unusual, according to statistics compiled by the National Center for Missing and Exploited Children, a national information clearing house. "We've tried from the beginning to tell everyone they don't have to live in fear," says Ernest Allen, the Center's president. Of 23,899 children reported missing to the Center since 1984, only 511 were abducted by strangers—most of the rest were runaways, or children taken in custody disputes. (Barbara Kantrowitz, "Keeping Hope Alive," *Newsweek*, November 1989, p. 95)

Step 1: (Make vocabulary simple)—

Cross out "quite" and use *very*.

Cross out "unusual" and use *rare*.

Cross out "abducted" and use *kidnapped*.

Step 2: (Eliminate flowery adjectives and adverbs)—

This step is included in steps #1 and #3.

Step 3: (Eliminate quotes and excess information)—

Cross out the first six words.

Cross out the phrase "a national information clearing house."

Leave out the quote "We've tried from . . . "

Leave out the explanation about runaways and kids taken in custody disputes (after a divorce).

Step 4: (Rewrite the information—reverse sentence order, combine ideas, and use your own adjectives and adverbs.)

Paraphrase: *The National Center for Missing and Exploited Children says that kidnapping by strangers is very rare. Only 511 kids out of almost 24,000 reported missing since 1984 were taken by strangers.*

How to Write Reports

Para-Practice II

Read the passages below; then write a paraphrase for each on the lines provided. Remember—keep the meaning of the originals, using your own words to retell them.

The issue of television in schools has centered on the advent of *Channel One,* a 12-minute daily news show produced by Whittle Communications. That program has been controversial because it includes 2 minutes of commercials. It now reaches 2,900 schools in 34 states; other jurisdictions, including California, Missouri, and New York, have banned it from their classrooms. While that quarrel continues undeterred, a group of private cable companies and public broadcasters has sharply increased educational programming. The cable companies see an opportunity to polish their image in local communities as well as hook in future audiences. The shows are commercial-free and many come with teachers' guides. The programmers are waiving their licensing rights so that educators can tape and reuse their shows for up to a year. And some operators, like Denver's Tele-Communications, Inc., will wire schools for cable without charge. (Connie Leslie, "The Second Blackboard," *Newsweek,* April 2, 1990, p. 48)

Paraphrase 1: _____

_____

_____

_____

_____

Early people presumably first realized time passed when they saw that they lived in a world of constant change. We have come to place a premium on measuring the flow of time—as if by measuring it we could begin to understand it. Devising accurate calendars and clocks, however, proved to be one of humanity's most elusive and protracted intellectual pursuits. The long struggle to affix numbers to the passage of time parallels our organizing ourselves in a complex, modern world. It began in the great civilizations that awakened five millennia ago along the life-giving rivers of the Middle East: in Sumer between the Tigris and Euphrates and in Egypt along the Nile. Drawn like most ancient people to the movements of the heavens and the changing seasons, the Babylonians developed a year of 360 days, then divided it into 12 lunar months of 30 days each. This was not a simple feat, since the sun and moon do not dance in step, the moon's cycles occurring approximately every 29½ days and the earth's every 365¼ days. (John Boslough, "The Enigma Of Time," *National Geographic,* March 1990, p. 111)

Paraphrase 2: _____

_____

_____

_____

_____

Name _____   Date _____

Para-Practice III

Paraphrase each of the passages below. If you use a specific fact, percentage, or important quote, you must credit the information.

Homeless children are the nation's shame. Their number has grown to 500,000 to 700,000, according to the National Coalition for the Homeless, a Washington-based advocacy group. They live in temporary shelters, in welfare hotels, in abandoned buildings, or on the street.

More than 200,000 of these children do not go to school regularly or at all. And since families with children are the fastest-growing segment of the homeless population, the number of children deprived of a chance to be educated is likely to increase.

A law enacted last July requires the secretary of education to make $3 million available to the states to help educate homeless children. (*The New York Times*, "Toward Educating the Homeless," February 21, 1988)

_____

_____

_____

_____

_____

Truancy is a growing problem in the Tenderloin, a poverty-stung section in downtown San Francisco. But an organization has offered a solution that requires only a change of clothes and truckloads of generosity. "When we ask children why they skip school, the No. 1 reason they give is that they are ashamed of their clothes and have no clean clothing," said Midge Wilson, the executive director of the Bay Area Women's Resource Center, which distributes free clothing

to about 900 homeless women and children in the Tenderloin. "It really makes a difference to their self-esteem if they can wear something brand new."

The clothes and other items are provided by an organization of more than 200 children's wear companies in the United States. The apparel group, which is based in New York, is called Kids in Distressed Situations, KIDS. It has also worked with relief organizations to provide new children's clothing and toys to refugees in

Ethiopia and to victims of volcanic eruptions in Colombia and severe floods in California. In the last three years, it has provided more than $3 million in clothing.

The group was founded in April 1985 by several clothing executives who were inspired by the entertainment industry's efforts to help victims of famine in Ethiopia. (*The New York Times*, "New Clothes Aid a Fight on Truancy," April 7, 1988)

_____

_____

_____

_____

_____

159

Para-Practice IV

Write a paraphrase for each passage below. Use the last sentence of the passage as the basis for your first sentence, and work back toward the beginning using your own words.

Twenty-five million years ago sequoias were common in what is now Texas and Pennsylvania and in areas that are now France and Japan. As the world's climate cooled and dried, however, the range of the sequoias shrank. Today coast redwoods are confined to a 30-mile-wide strip of rugged land that runs some 500 miles along the Pacific from the Oregon border to south of Big Sur. The thickest, tallest forests are in California's Humboldt and Del Norte counties, where whole groves average 300 feet.

The giant sequoias are even more isolated. These trees grow not in a continuous strip of forest but in 75 mostly small groves. All are found along the western slopes of the Sierra Nevada of east central California. Despite their relatively small numbers, giant sequoias seem to be more tolerant of environmental extremes than their cousins. The trees can withstand 20-foot snowfalls and zero-degree temperatures. (Doug Stewart, "Green Giants," *Discover*, April 1990, p. 64)

_____

_____

_____

_____

_____

Spiders have no equal when it comes to engineering with silk. They catch their prey in silk webs, protect their eggs in silk sacs, drift on strands of silk at altitudes up to 2,500 feet. Spiders even communicate over silk; courting males rhythmically pluck the strings of a female's web. These creatures are among the earliest predators to have evolved on land, and clearly silk was important to their success. The key to their skills is an organ called a spinneret: an appendage of glands, ducts, and spigots that evolved on the spider's hindquarters. So the recent identification of a fossil spinneret from 380 million years ago is not only the earliest firm evidence for spiders, pushing back the date of their appearance by at least 60 million years, but also an important new landmark in the evolution of species. ("Up Front: Ancient Spiders," *Discover*, April 1990, p.21)

_____

_____

_____

_____

_____

How to Write Reports

Transformation

Paraphrasing works. No doubt about that. It's fast, accurate, and gives a personal touch to reports.

But there's another technique used in report writing that's just as helpful—**transformation**.

Instead of taking a long, complicated passage and making it more compact, this technique requires that you take short bits of information and expand them into sentences, then combine the sentences into paragraphs.

Here's how: Let's say you had a notecard like the one below. You could transform the separate bits of information into intelligent sentences and make a small paragraph for a report on environmental pollution.

You could go from this:

```
        Disposable Diapers
1. produce 90 times more garbage
   than cloth diapers.
2. take 500 years to decompose
3. encourage the throwaway habit
```

. . . to this: "Some sources consider disposable diapers to be a serious hazard to the environment of the United States because they are piling up by the millions. Disposables create 90 times more garbage than cloth diapers, and when dumped take almost 500 years to decompose. But possibly the worst side effect of disposable diapers is the way they help keep up the habit Americans have of using something, then tossing the plastic container in the trash."

Name _____ Date _____

Be a Transformer

To transform bits of information into a complete paragraph, you need to:

1. Write a general topic sentence that explains what the rest of the paragraph is about.

2. Add subjects, verbs, pronouns, and adjectives to the basic facts to make sentences.

3. Combine sentences. (If you need them, you can use some connecting words like *and, also, first, next,* and *finally.*)

EXERCISE

Transform the information on the notecard below into a complete four-sentence paragraph.

Little League Baseball

1. Began in 1939 at Williamsport, Pennsylvania
2. Today—almost 11,000 leagues and 3 million players
3. Law signed by Gerald Ford, President, in 1974 allowing girls to play
   a. players must be 8-12 years old
   b. 12-15 players per team
   c. need parents' permission and physical exam by a doctor

PARAGRAPH

_____

_____

_____

_____

_____

_____

_____

Transformer II

Transform the brief facts and information on the notecards below and on the next page into complete paragraphs.

Reindeer

1. 3½ feet high, 300 pounds, elklike horns, poor vision.

2. Used for food, clothing, and as a four-legged tractor to pull loads.

3. Tracked by bells around neck and radar collars (not herded like cows).

4. Been part of Lapland's culture for 4,000 years.

_____

_____

_____

_____

_____

_____

_____

_____

_____

(continued)

Transformer II *(continued)*

Future Trains

1. New trains are called ''maglev'' trains
   a. Magnets lift trains off tracks

2. High speed—300 mph

3. High cost—over $1 billion to develop

4. Look like airplanes without wings

5. Leader in development—West Germany

_____

_____

_____

_____

_____

_____

_____

_____

_____

_____

Name _____ Date _____

Transformer III

Transform the information on the notecard below into a complete paragraph.
(Use a topic sentence.)

McDonald's Restaurants

1. Started by Mr. Ray Kroc in 1955 in Des Plaines, Illinois.

2. Used speed, efficiency, and quality in product.

3. Realized that more restaurants = more $—result was a ''franchise.''

4. A franchise uses the name of the original company—helps train new restaurant owners.

5. Ray Kroc established Hamburger University to train McDonald's workers.

6. Bought the name from the McDonald brothers in San Bernardino, California, in 1953.

7. Most successful restaurant chain in the world.

_____

_____

_____

_____

_____

_____

_____

_____

_____

_____

Name _____ Date _____

Transformer IV

Transform the notes on the "cards" below into two paragraphs. Each should have a topic sentence and transitions like *and, also, furthermore, first,* and *second.*

Peace Corps History

1. President Kennedy's idea—1960.

2. Peace Corps meant to help poor people around the world.

3. Sept. 1961 Congress established Peace Corps.

4. Peace Corps declined from 1968-80.

5. In 1981 President Reagan reestablished Peace Corps.

6. In last 30 years 122,000 people served 99 countries.

Peace Corps Criticism

1. Some said Peace Corps created to make Pres. Kennedy look good.

2. Others said Peace Corps volunteers were unskilled/not helpful.

3. Opponents called it ''Kennedy's Kiddie Korps.''

4. Today—Peace Corps is in 68 countries.

5. Also, Peace Corps volunteers ''adopt'' a classroom in U.S. and send letters/photos about Peace Corps.

_____

_____

_____

_____

_____

_____

_____

_____

(continued)

Transformer IV *(continued)*

_____

_____

_____

_____

_____

_____

_____

_____

How to Write Reports

Section 6: Using Quotes

Name _____ Date _____

Get the Quotes

Some reports are special. They're interesting—full of new information and solid facts. And they almost always contain a special ingredient . . . **quotes**.

A **quote** is a statement by an expert that says something interesting or specifically important about a topic.

Let's say you're reading and taking notes on the subject of *dental surgery,* your report topic, and you find a statement by a leading dental surgeon that says:

"Almost 30 percent of the dental surgeries done today are not really necessary."

You've just struck gold! This interesting piece of information will make your readers sit up and take notice.

Now you have to ask:

- Why are these surgeries unnecessary?
- Who performs these unnecessary surgeries?
- How can a patient know whether surgery is necessary or not?

These questions can add to your report. They can cause you to uncover even more interesting information . . . and then more . . . and more.

Just this one quote can lead to a set of facts that the average report just won't have.

Quotes can make your report:

- more *believable* because of statements by "experts."
- more *interesting* by bringing in new facts.
- more *distinctive* because it won't be just a long summary out of an encyclopedia.
- more *up-to-date* because an expert knows what's happening now!

Name _____ Date _____

Which Quotes to Use?

All quotes are not created equal. Some contain specific information, while others are vague and empty.

A quote that says: "There are a lot of cyclists on America's highways," is not as informative as one that says: "*Twenty million* cyclists took to the highway last year."

The second quote gives a number . . . 20 million.

The first quote is just a loose guess.

EXERCISE

Put a **V** next to the vague quote in each numbered pair below, and put an **I** by the most informative quote.

1 a. _____ "Some giant squids can get pretty big."

  b. _____ "The giant squid can grow to a length of 55 feet."

2 a. _____ "Australia exports a lot of wool."

  b. _____ "Australia is the world's leading exporter of wool."

3 a. _____ "Aborigines lived in Australia 40,000 years before white settlers arrived."

  b. _____ "The Aborigines were in Australia many years before the white settlers came."

4 a. _____ "Most of Australia's people live in the southeast section of the country."

  b. _____ "About 80 percent of Australia's people live in the southeast section of the country."

5 a. _____ "A lot of immigrants have been allowed into Australia since World War II."

  b. _____ "Australia has allowed 4.75 million immigrants to cross its shores since World War II."

How to Write Reports

Expert Opinion

Just like quotes, all opinions are not created equal, either.

If the postman says, "Football takes more brains than muscle," and your uncle, who played for the Pittsburgh Steelers, says, "Football takes more brains than muscle," whom would you listen to and believe?

The postman may be right, but he never played the game.

The same thing goes for quotes you use in reports. If ten quotes are given in a particular article, book, or video, choose the ones that come from the most informed people: the **experts**.

EXERCISE

Put an **X** next to the quote in each numbered pair below that comes from the expert.

1 a. _____ "Teens who do best with stress are those who like themselves," says Dr. Antoinette Saunders, director of the Stress Education Center for Children.

  b. _____ "If kids like themselves, they'll do better in handling stress," says Mr. Altman, the city librarian.

2 a. _____ "Yawning is the body's way of keeping you alert in situations where you can't go to sleep," says psychologist Ronald Baenninger of Temple University.

  b. _____ "Yawning helps people stay awake, like when I'm driving all night," says Agnes Lugnut, truck driver.

3 a. _____ "It is clear that there is a great need for substances that will help people who have had severe loss of memory," says science researcher John Disterhoft of Northwestern University.

  b. _____ "A lot of people have lost their memory, and what they need is a drug or a pill to help them," says Milton Ibee, the druggist.

Choose the Quotes

Each notecard below contains quotes on a specific topic. But some of the quotes are unsuitable for a good report because they don't give enough information, or they don't give an interesting opinion, or they aren't specific.

Circle the letters of the most effective quotes on each card below.

---

a. ''Writing reports is a complex task.''

b. ''New technology has given students many more research tools to work with. Computer data banks, for instance, can provide information on 1,000 topics with the push of a few buttons.''

c. ''By writing about a topic that personally means something to you, the 'chore' of report writing is eliminated.''

d. ''With 110,000 high schools in the United States, there will be a lot of reports written this year.''

---

a. ''Everyone should try to be healthy.''

b. ''Being healthy doesn't mean just being physically fit. It means having a good attitude, believing in yourself, and understanding your role in the family, school, and community.''

c. ''Physical exercise can help your mental outlook by relaxing you and by making you feel strong and vigorous.''

d. ''A 120-pound teenager burns 65 calories per hour while reading, 260 calories per hour walking, and 456 calories per hour playing basketball.''

e. ''A person should eat a balanced diet.''

Quotes in Your Notes

When you find a quote you want to use in your report, write it out, word for word, on a *separate* notecard. Then put a dash (—) after the quote and write the speaker's name. Then list the source information at the bottom of the card: author of the article (or book), title of article (or book), name of magazine (*Time, Life,* etc.) or name of publisher (for a book), publication date, and page number where you found the quote.

Example:

```
''At one month, many drug-addicted babies
function at the same level as a two-day-old
infant.''

— Dr. Ira Chasnoff, pediatrician at North-
western Memorial Hospital in Chicago.

Bregman, Mark, ''Crack Babies: Abused Before
Birth,'' Scholastic Choices, November
1989, p. 13
```

Your turn. Read the paragraph on the next page, copy the first and last sentence of the quote on the "notecard," then write the speaker's name and all the necessary source information at the bottom of the "card."

(continued)

Name _____ Date _____

Quotes in Your Notes *(continued)*

"Ronnie Barnes: Athletic Trainer of Champions" (no author given) *Career World,* November '89, p. 8

Ronnie Barnes manages and supervises a staff of assistants. He reports the status of injuries to the NFL office and does the budgeting for supplies and salaries.

Barnes feels the field of ath-letic training is wide open for today's students. He says, "Jobs now exist at all colleges, many high schools, and even some junior and middle schools. In addition, corporate fitness cen-ters and sports medicine clinics are growing by leaps and bounds. It is particularly wide open for minorities. I recommend high schoolers take a strong science program, particularly biology and chemistry, and also develop good math skills."

Quote:

Source:

Making Quotes

Each paragraph below contains one or more quotes. Copy at least one quote from each paragraph onto the "notecards" provided. Include the speaker's name and occupation, then the source information at the bottom of each card.

Needham, Dick, "Annie Gets Her Guns," *Ski,* February '89, p. 76

Last season, Mont Sainte-Anne logged in roughly 640,000 skier visits (about the same number, to put that into perspective, as Mount Snow, Vt.), catapulting the area to No. 1 in Canadian popularity.

It wasn't always that way. "We were always considered a sleeping giant," says [co-owner] Filion, "and then, in 1982, we discovered snowmaking, invested $8 million in a plant and machinery, and sat back to count the return."

"Since then," Filion adds, "we've grown from a mountain with great, if unknown, potential to a major force in Canadian skiing." As testimony to all this, Filion points out, increasing numbers of skiers are opting to stay at the mountain (most at huge Hotel Chateau Mont Sainte-Anne) rather than in Quebec City 45 minutes down the road.

Quote:

Source:

How to Write Reports

Making Quotes *(continued)*

Roman, Mark, "Tornado Tracker," *Discover,* June 1989, p. 57

Weather researchers know that most often these spiraling killers [tornadoes] appear out of the dense, dark wall of clouds that cloaks the engine of a severe thunderstorm. They also know that the violent funnels tend to form in or near the updraft of air that rushes from ground level into the void at the storm's core. But they know little else for certain.

"We know a lot more than we did 15 years ago," acknowledges [meteorologist Howard] Bluestein, "but there are major gaps in our knowledge. We don't really know why tornadoes occur."

Quote:

Source:

How to Write Reports

Using Quotes

When you write a quote into the body of your report, you don't just pull out a notecard and start copying. You have to change the form a little bit. Here's how:

Suppose the notecard says:

> ''It appears that some kind of small-scale cultivation of cereals took place about 12,000 years ago.''
>
> — Romana Unger-Hamilton, archaeologist from University College in London, England

In your report you must write:

Romana Unger-Hamilton, archaeologist from University College in London, England, says, "It appears that some kind of small-scale cultivation of cereals took place about 12,000 years ago."

(continued)

Using Quotes *(continued)*

EXERCISE

Rewrite the quote from the notecard below onto the lines provided using the form shown on the previous page: author's name and occupation, then the word *says* or *said,* then the quote.

Quote: ''The more alcohol consumed in a lifetime, the less strength of the heart and the less strength of the muscles.''

—Emanuel Rubin, pathologist from Jefferson Medical College, Philadelphia, PA

_____

_____

_____

_____

_____

_____

Using More Quotes

Rewrite the quotes below as if you were writing them into the body of a report.

Quote: "No scientist has complete and accurate data on how much pollution it will take to make life on this planet impossible."

—Dr. Peter Holcomb, scientist at U.W. Labs in Paris, France.

_____

_____

_____

_____

Quote: "Kids today are emotionally stronger than kids were 40 years ago because they must make much tougher decisions under a variety of stressful situations."

—Dr. Marilyn Repshire, head of the child development program at Burns Clinical University, Agnes, Australia.

_____

_____

_____

_____

Giving Credit

You don't have to be dressed in black and be lurking in the dark to be called a thief. All you have to do is use other people's facts and opinions in a report that you hand in at school. This kind of stealing is called **plagiarism** and is so subtle that a lot of people don't really know they've committed this crime until it's too late.

Example: A person opens a magazine, sees a good quote from an expert, and writes it down, never acknowledging who actually said it. That's **plagiarism**.

To avoid being called a thief, a writer has to give **credit** to quotes that are borrowed.

Here's how: In parentheses at the end of a quote that you've used, simply write the last name of the author who originally wrote the quote, along with the page number of the quote. That's it!

Example: Madam C. J. Walker, the first black female millionaire, said, "The girls and women of our race must not be afraid to take hold of business enterprises." (Doyle, p. 24)

Doyle is the author of the article. p. 24 is the page number.

This style of crediting information was developed by the Modern Language Association (MLA) and has helped millions of writers to avoid **plagiarism.** Use this method with specific quotes and you cannot be called a thief.

Note: Another step you need to take later on in the report writing process is to list the magazine or book or other source from which you borrowed the quote. We will learn how that is done later.

Name _____   Date _____

Credit for Quotes I

Rewrite the quotes below onto the lines provided. Write them as if you were including them in a report, giving credit to the author of the article.

(Remember: Use the author's last name and the page number)

Pit Bulldogs

Quote: ''These dogs have the jaw strength of a lion. They are time bombs, and their owners don't know what they have until it's too late.''

— David Davis, lawyer

Source: Reynolds, C.V., ''Man's Worst Friend,'' <u>Discover</u> magazine, Jan. '88, p. 46

_____

_____

_____ (   )

Tanning Salons

Quote: ''There's no way for a consumer to know how much ultraviolet radiation is coming out of the tanning unit.''

— Warwick Morison, M.D., from Johns Hopkins University

Source: Slom, Celia, ''Tanning Salons: A Winter Hazard,'' <u>McCall's</u>, Feb. '90, p. 94

_____

_____

_____ (   )

181   *How to Write Reports*

Name _____ Date _____

Credit for Quotes II

Rewrite the quotes below into the correct form for a report giving the proper credit to the author.

Microwave Ovens

Quote: ''The microwave is what I call an attractive hazard.''

— Louis Slesin, editor of <u>Microwave</u>

Source: Shapiro, Laura, ''The Zap Generation,'' <u>Newsweek</u>, February 26, 1990, p. 56

_____

_____

_____

_____

The Sun

Quote: ''If a good case could be made for the sun's influence on weather, then the fact alone would be more important than anything else studied in solar-terrestrial physics.''

— Peter Foukal, solar physicist

Source: Bartusiak, Marcia, ''The Sunspot Syndrome,'' <u>Discover</u>, November 1989, p. 45

_____

_____

_____

_____

How to Write Reports

Section 7: Crediting Information

Name _____ Date _____

Credit the Facts

Quotes aren't the only things you borrow and use in a report. Often you use facts—percentages, numbers, amounts, dates, times, and locations that are so unique and hard to find that you need to give them **credit.**

Example: Not having a home can be a terrible thing—to have to live in the streets, sleep on church steps, and beg money for food would be humiliating and frightening. Today 600,000 to 1.2 million people live this way in America. (*Life* magazine, Dec. '87, p. 44)

Someone researched the homeless and came up with the numbers 600,000 to 1.2 million. If you want to use these numbers in your report, it is only fair to give credit to the author *or* to the magazine (or other source) that published the information. Otherwise it might look as if you researched the homeless and came up with the information yourself, which would be a lie.

This kind of lying in a report is called **plagiarism,** or "stealing,"

EXERCISE

In the parentheses at the end of the paragraph below, write the name of the author and the page on which the specific facts were found. Use the source to the right of the paragraph to get the credit information.

Influenza is alive and deadly in the United States today. But most people don't die from the "flu." They die from complications caused by the flu, that often develop into pneumonia. Nearly 29 people out of every 100,000 who get the flu end up dead from pneumonia. (   )

Brody, Robert
"Colds That Linger"
Health magazine
Feb. 1990, p. 63

184

Crediting I

To give **credit** to an author whose information you've borrowed, write his or her name in parentheses after the facts along with the page number where the information was found.

EXERCISE

The three paragraphs below include information that should be **credited** to the author (or to the source if the author's name isn't given). Find the author's name in the source information to the right of each paragraph and write the name between the parentheses. Don't forget to include the page number where the facts were found. (The first one is done as an example.)

The destructive power of a volcano is terrifying. When Mount St. Helens exploded from deep within the earth in 1980, it left a wake of death across the state of Washington: 57 people were missing or dead, along with 5,000 black-tailed deer, 1,500 elk, and 300 black bear. (Heacox, p. 112)

Heacox, Kim
"The Rebirth of Mount St. Helens"
National Geographic Traveler
Spring 1987
p. 112

In 1849 every person's dream became possible. Gold was discovered in California, lots of it, and all you had to do was dig it out of the ground. Within a few years almost a quarter of a million people had invaded California. In just 7 years, $400 million worth of gold was dug from the earth or scooped from the rivers.
( )

Kiester, Edwin
"Boomtown Chronicles"
National Geographic Traveler
Spring 1987
p. 49

Walking is humanity's oldest sport. It requires little fuss or strength and can be an enjoyable activity for anyone of any age. But to keep it fun, you must take great care of your feet, and that means buying a good pair of walking shoes. But which ones should you buy? Over 200 types of walking shoes are on the market today.
( ).Which means that soon the hardest thing about walking will be knowing which type of shoe to buy!

Kaufman, Elizabeth
"Shoe Biz"
Health
Sept. '89
p. 60

Crediting II

Below are three paragraphs that could be used in three different reports. They each contain specific information that should be **credited** with the author's name and the page number on which the information was found.

Next to each paragraph is the name of the source from which the facts were borrowed. Find the author's name and write it, along with the page number, in the parentheses after each paragraph.

Because there has been a lot of debate in the past few years about the subject of abortion, women's rights groups are growing in number and gaining in financial power. As of 1989, the National Abortion Rights Action League gained 50,000 new members and took in an additional $1 million in dues and support money.
(   )

Carlson, M.
"Can Pro-Choicers Prevail?"
Time magazine
August 14, '89
p. 28

Teenage students who drive are being put to the test. Not a driver's test, but a social studies test, an English test, and even math, health, and science tests. Why? Because if students do poorly and flunk out of school, many states are passing laws to take away their driving licenses. In June of 1988 West Virginia passed such a law, and though there are complications, it has kept 1,644 kids from choosing to drop out.
(   )

Hanauer, Amy
"Hit the Books, Jack"
Seventeen
Feb. 1990
p. 42

The deer herds in some parts of America are expanding so fast that the animals are crowding out their food supply. Many are starving. Some people feel that many more thousands will die soon if something isn't done. So wildlife groups are moving deer from overpopulated areas to less crowded feeding grounds. The problem is that as many as 50 percent of the deer are dying from the effects of being moved.
(   )

Leslie, Paul
"The Bambi Boom"
Science World
October 20, '89
p. 12

Credit, Anyone?

It's important to give credit where credit is due, but you can't really credit *every drop* of information you squeeze out of your sources. Your report would be nothing but a confusing list of credits: (Mowry, p. 9), (Judith p. 46), (Fullmer, p. 9), (Richter, p. 5), (Burkett, p. 57), (Steege, p. 101), (Tabke, p. 4) . . .

You have to decide which information is specific or unique or recent enough to earn an official credit. The information below, for example, would not get a specific credit line:

- The Nile River runs from south to north.

- The sun is about 93 million miles away from earth.

- The moon is about 240,000 miles from earth.

- President Kennedy was assassinated in 1963.

- The *Challenger* spacecraft exploded in 1984.

- The Berlin Wall was dismantled in 1989.

All of this information has been mentioned dozens of times in newspapers, magazines, encyclopedias, and many other reference books. It's **general knowledge**. It's nothing new and recently discovered. It is not information that would cause discussion. So it should not be credited in a report.

You *can*, however, list the source (book, magazine, newspaper, etc.) from which you got this general background information on a page called "Works Consulted" at the end of the report. That way you can't be called for plagiarism. You have acknowledged the source without splattering your report with credit notations. (How to put together a "Works Consulted" page is discussed later.)

To Credit or Not to Credit

Decide which information below is specific and needs a credit notation and which is simply general knowledge. Then mark the general knowledge with a **G**, and mark with a **C** the information that is specific and should be credited.

Example: __G__ The Berlin Wall was built in 1948.

__C__ In 28 years, 190 people have died trying to get past the Berlin Wall.

1. _____ Germany lost World War II.

2. _____ Berlin was divided into East and West after World War II.

3. _____ The Berlin Wall was torn down in November of 1989.

4. _____ The population of West Germany will increase as East Germans move into the "free" West Germany.

5. _____ The West Berlin government gave $55 as "greeting money" to each person who crossed over the border from East Germany when the Wall first came down.

6. _____ In the first 24 hours after the Berlin Wall was opened, 1,500 people registered as permanent citizens of West Germany.

7. _____ Germany has been in two world wars during the 20th century.

8. _____ East Germany was under a Communist form of government before the Wall was opened.

Name _____   Date _____

What Gets Credit?

The difference between general knowledge and specific information is like the difference between a mutt and a purebred poodle—one is common, while the other requires credentials.

Decide which bits of information below need "credentials" or credits, and which are general knowledge. Then mark the general knowledge with a **G** and mark the information that needs a credit with the letter **C**.

1. _____ The Pilgrims landed at Plymouth Rock.

2. _____ Canada is a country located to the north of the United States.

3. _____ Almost 90 percent of Canada's population lives along the route established by the Canadian Railroad.

4. _____ Bill Coo, Canadian writer and railroad man, has said, "Seventy-five percent of the people who ride the Canadian Railroad are not Canadian."

5. _____ George Washington was the first president of the United States.

6. _____ Canada has an organization called the Royal Canadian Mounted Police.

7. _____ These people are nicknamed "Mounties."

8. _____ Canada contains one third of all the fresh water on earth.

9. _____ Western Canada is a vast area of treeless plains.

10. _____ The Rocky Mountains run for many miles through western Canada.

11. _____ When laying the track for the Canadian Railroad through the Canadian Shield, dynamiters used three tons of dynamite a day.

12. _____ The last spike on the Canadian Railroad was driven on November 7, 1885.

13. _____ Most people in Montreal speak French.

14. _____ Laborers who laid the track for the Canadian Railroad were once paid 15 cents an hour.

Section 8: Writing Conclusions

The End

Writing a report is like riding a bike—the most important thing to know is how to *stop*.

A person is reading a report, for example, enjoying the things she's learning, when all of a sudden—WHAM! She runs smack into the bottom of the page. No more quotes. No more summaries, percentages, or facts.

THE END.

This slamming on of the brakes is brutal. People want to coast to a stop with a good **conclusion** that wraps things up and brings the report to a close.

Here's an example—a conclusion for a report on **bicycle safety**:

"With more and more people driving bikes for pleasure, for exercise, and for basic transportation, our roads and parks and public sidewalks are becoming places where bike safety is very important. Classes are being offered by local police forces, parents are taking an active role in teaching their children about bike safety, and many schools are promoting careful bicycle use. With this kind of support, the people who pedal their way to work or to school or down to the store can be more sure of getting there and back without causing injury to themselves or to others."

This **conclusion** works for two reasons:

1. It summarizes a few points covered in the report (police-offered bike safety classes, parent involvement, and safety courses at school).

2. It gives a general, commonsense opinion (bike safety is important) that provides the reader with a logical assumption after all the facts have been read.

Meet the General

What is a general *opinion* statement doing in a report, you ask? Good question! After all, reports are supposed to tell the facts, not someone's opinion.

But we're not talking about the report now; we're talking about the **conclusion** to a report. As the word implies, a conclusion is a decision or a logical assumption made *after reading all the facts.*

Besides, a **general opinion statement** is almost a fact—that is, it is so absolutely obvious that no sane person would argue with it, and thus it is considered an accepted truth.

For example, you could say: "Environmental pollution must be stopped."

or: "Predicting earthquakes more accurately could save Thousands of lives each year."

or: "Roller coasters will keep thrilling riders of all ages as long as there are amusement parks and willing passengers."

These are opinions that are so obviously true that they are beyond argument. Such opinions can help you make great endings to good reports. They wrap things up and make sense out of all the facts and figures that the reader has just digested.

EXERCISE

On the lines below, write a G.O.S. (general opinion statement) about how much most people love potato chips.

_____

_____

_____

Name _____ Date _____

Find the G.O.S.

Read the conclusions below, then underline the one statement that clearly is the **general opinion statement** in each paragraph.

1. Newspaper cartoons have been part of American journalism for over 100 years. People who catch up on the news or read the sports scores usually can't help but skip over to the cartoon page to get a quick laugh from the adventures of their favorite character. No matter how busy or stressful the world becomes, people will always want to chuckle at something funny; that's why cartoons will be around as long as there are newspapers.

2. Though it has taken many decades for women to work their way into jobs traditionally held by men, thousands of women today work construction, drive trucks, cut timber, break horses, mine ore, and fish the coasts of North America. They are determined to make a living at whatever they choose, and in the process women have changed a lot of the ideas about who should be doing what. No one doubts that what we think today about women in the working world will change even more as women become more involved in politics, law, religion, business, and education.

3. When the Pilgrims landed on the cold, wooded shores of North America in the 1600's, the land was new and untamed and even frightening. But these travelers from England faced it and built small cabins and grew simple crops and eventually survived. Little did they know that their religious outlook, their desire for new land, and their determination would lay the foundation for a country that has always been a home for "pilgrims."

4. Jane Addams, winner of the Nobel Peace Prize, social worker, author, student, and political leader, stood for one thing: the dignity and welfare of all people. She worked long hours to see that women and children did not have to. She spent years organizing groups to fight poverty and ignorance. And she built a community outreach program called Hull House, in Chicago, that stood as a model for cities around the world. It is no wonder that Jane Addams is considered one of the greatest Americans who ever lived.

Generally Speaking

Below are 20 statements of opinion. Some are general opinion statements, and others are very controversial and would cause much argument. Mark only the general opinion statements with the initials **G.O.S.** Leave the rest blank.

Example: **G.O.S.** Abandoned pets are a problem in towns and cities everywhere.

_____ Everybody hates abandoned pets.

1. _____ Buying a new car is always a time of excitement for a family.

2. _____ Buying a new car is a financial mistake.

3. _____ Teenage are taking on a lot of responsibility when they drive a car onto the highway.

4. _____ Teenage drivers are the worst drivers in the world.

5. _____ Driver education programs are basically unnecessary.

6. _____ Traveling 500 to 600 miles per day in a car can lead to extreme fatigue.

7. _____ Taking an airplane is usually more efficient when traveling over 200 miles.

8. _____ Airplane accidents are tragic events that get a lot of coverage on television.

9. _____ Though airplane travel is the safest in the world, most people feel nervous during their first flight.

10. _____ The Wright brothers were not only daring but also hardworking.

11. _____ The cheapest way to travel is to walk.

12. _____ Nature trails cost too much money to maintain for the small number of people who use them.

13. _____ Backwoods camping is a hobby that has gone out of style.

14. _____ One of the biggest stretches of wilderness left in the world is in Canada.

15. _____ Keeping the wilderness areas of our planet safe from pollution is a responsibility we all share.

16. _____ President Teddy Roosevelt did the world a favor when he supported the idea of creating national parks.

17. _____ Most city people like a chance to walk in the park.

18. _____ People shouldn't jog alone after dark.

19. _____ Jogging is the best way to spend leisure time.

20. _____ Smoking is clearly a health hazard.

Name _____ Date _____

Opinion, Please

Endings are harder than beginnings.

- Starting a two-mile run is easier than running the last lap.
- Beginning a trip to Grandma's is easier than saying goodbye.
- Beginning a report is easier than ending it.

So practice **concluding** a report by writing a **general opinion statement** (G.O.S.) for each of the topics below. Remember: A G.O.S. is an obviously true opinion.

1. Cliff Divers . . .

_____

_____

2. Television News . . .

_____

_____

_____

3. Dr. Martin Luther King . . .

_____

_____

_____

4. Littering . . .

_____

_____

_____

Your Turn

Using the information listed below each topic, write a short **conclusion** that wraps things up for the reader.

Example: Topic: "Baseball—The All-American Sport"
    a. easy-to-learn rules
    b. players can be any size
    c. inexpensive
    d. family can participate
    e. competitive
    f. brings folks together

Conclusion: "America's love of sports has kept baseball a popular activity for kids and adults of all ages. Any kid of any size can learn the game in an afternoon and play with friends or family with very little to spend on equipment and supplies. The game brings people together and puts just enough competition into things to make it interesting. With all these elements going for it, baseball has a solid future."

1. Topic: "Swimming"

    a. healthy
    b. inexpensive (trunks and pool fee)
    c. life-saving possibilities

_____

_____

_____

_____

_____

2. Topic: Westward Expansion of United States

    a. free land
    b. freedom for slaves
    c. making money in business
    d. adventure

_____

_____

_____

_____

_____

_____

Name _____ Date _____

In Conclusion

If you need to, visit the library and find just enough general information about each topic below to write a four- or five-sentence **conclusion** paragraph with a **general opinion statement** to wrap things up.

1. Topic: MARIE CURIE

_____

_____

_____

_____

_____

_____

_____

_____

2. Topic: *SPUTNIK*

_____

_____

_____

_____

_____

_____

_____

_____

_____

Section 9: Reveal the Source

Name _____ Date _____

Reveal the Source

The last step in completing a report is to reveal your sources for those who might want to check your facts or read more about your topic.

The best way to do this is to make two lists. One list, called the **"Works Cited"** page (*cited* means "referred to"), should contain all the library catalog information on each work you quoted from or took specific facts and figures from: author's name, title of article, title of source, place of publication, and name of publisher (for a book), volume number, date, and page numbers of short pieces like magazine and newspaper articles.

The other list (a separate page) is exactly like the "Works Cited" page except that it includes *all the works you read* or watched or listened to while researching your report, including the ones you *didn't* quote or borrow from specifically but used for general knowledge. This page is called the **"Works Consulted"** page.

All the entries on both of these pages are listed alphabetically by author's last name or by the first word in the title of the article or source if the author's name is not given. (Skip the words *a, an,* and *the* when alphabetizing by title.)

And take note that on the "Works Cited" page you do not write the numbers of the exact pages you borrowed from, because those page numbers are mentioned in the body of your report within the credit information listed there. (But do include the page numbers on which an entire newspaper or magazine article appeared.)

Examples of how a video, pamphlet, book, newspaper, and magazine should be listed on both the "Works Cited" page and the "Works Consulted" page are shown below:

Video . . . *AIDS: Fears and Facts,* Spinnaker Software Corporation, 1987.

Pamphlet . . . *Facts About AIDS,* American Red Cross, November, 1988.

Book . . . Lerner, Ethan A., *Understanding AIDS,* Minneapolis, Lerner Publications, 1987.

Newspaper . . . Russell, Ron, "State OK's School AIDS Policy," *Detroit News,* April 9, 1986, pp. 17–18.

Magazine . . . Ullman, Linn, "Time To Talk," *Seventeen,* September 1989, pp. 112–113.

Notes: 1. Always begin your source list at the left margin and indent the second line about five spaces or ½″.

2. Center page titles—"Works Cited" and "Works Consulted"—at the top of the page.

(continued)

Reveal the Source *(continued)*

3. Follow correct rules of punctuation: underline or italicize titles of books (including encyclopedias and other reference books), names of magazines, names of newspapers, and titles of pamphlets and videos. Put quotation marks around titles of articles in magazines and encyclopedias.

4. When listing a book by more than one author, start with the last name of the author who is listed first on the book cover, followed by that authors's first name (and a comma); then write the full name of the second author.

   EXAMPLE: Johnson, Jean, and Al Smith.

5. When in doubt about how to compile a list of sources, consult this text:

   Gibaldi, Joseph, and Walter S. Achtert, *MLA Handbook for Writers of Research Papers,* Second Edition, New York, Modern Language Association of America, 1984.

CHAPTER 5:

A MODEL REPORT

A Model Report

When you're learning a new skill, it sometimes helps to have a model, a sample of what the finished product *should* look like. The following pages contain something even better—a step-by-step example of the entire process of report writing: gathering information, organizing that information, and actually writing that information into a publishable report.

An eighth-grade student from Burns High School in Burns, Wyoming, built a report around the subject of Cheerleading, a sport that she was involved in personally, and a subject that has been in the news because of the danger created by the new approach to cheerleading that many colleges and high schools have taken. Also, the writer thought that the "all-female or all-male" issue in sports made her report on cheerleading even more important.

The notecards, the outline, and the complete report are included here for your benefit. Examine them and use these examples to improve your own work. Your subject will be different, your approach and style will be your own, but the thoughtfulness and hard work shown by this piece of writing is required of all good reports and should be a main ingredient in any report you do.

Notecards
"Yea for Cheerleading"

NOTECARDS for report: "Yea For Cheerleading"

by: Gena Sandberg
     Burns High School
     Burns, Wyoming

```
History: Beginnings of Cheerleading

— Ancient civilizations—cheered warriors
— 1860's—Ivy League colleges
— 1898 at Univ. of Minnesota
— first ''yell marshal'' = John Campbell

— first cheer = ''Rah, Rah, Rah,
                    Sis, Boom, Bah''

  Source: Go, Fight, Win!, by Francis Shepard,
          New York, Delacorte Press, 1981
```

```
History: Today #1

— Dangerous activity
  — 4,954 emergencies in 1980
  — 6,911 emer. in 1986
    = 40% rise

— Example = Janice Thompson, killed

         Source: ''Is Cheerleading Getting Too
         Dangerous?'' by Alison Frankel, Seventeen,
         Sept. '87, p. 56
```

(continued)

Notecards *(continued)*
"Yea for Cheerleading"

History: Today #2

— Should Cheerleading be a ''sport''?
— (High school athletic associations
   see it as ''activity'' like band & chorus)

Quote: ''It isn't just yelling anymore. Your hair
      is pulled back, and you're out there to sweat.''
      (Lisa Anderson in ''Is Cheerleading Getting
      Too Dangerous?'' p. 60)

History: Today #3

— Cheerl. should have rules
Quote: ''It's like basketball—you can't play if everyone
      has different rules.''
      (Teressa Weant, Coach at Lemon Bay H.S. in
      Englewood Florida, in ''Is Cheerleading Getting
      Too Dangerous?'' p. 60)

(continued)

How to Write Reports

Notecards *(continued)*
"Yea for Cheerleading"

History: Today #4 . . . rules con't.

— No rules means unequal opportunities

Quote: ''We're a safety-minded school, so we're strict
about rules. But when other squads come in and do
three-tier pyramids, my girls all say, 'Why can't
we do that?' If there were something set, then all
schools would have to abide.''
(Teressa Weant, in ''Is Cheerleading . . .?''
p. 60)

History: Today #5 . . . rules con't.

— No rules means no limits + unsafe
— Sponsors should be trained also

Quote: ''Some of the coaches are extremely talented
people who believe in what they're doing. But
there are others who look at cheerleading like a
sponsor-type thing, meaning they do little more
than make sure the girls are on the bus on time.
The way cheerleading must go in the future is that
coaches must be trained.''
(Melanie Butler, coach/Huntington H.S.,
W. Virginia, in ''Is Cheerl . . ?'' p. 60)

(continued)

                   How to Write Reports

Notecards *(continued)*
"Yea for Cheerleading"

Cheerleading Camps #1

— Learn new skills
  — tumbling
  — stunts
  — mounts
  — cheers and chants
  — learn teamwork
— Social skills
  — meet people from all areas and walks of life
— Learn from best cheerleading coaches in the nation

Cheerleading Camps #2

— Cheerleading Organization
  — U.S.A. (United Spirit Association)
  — hosts 82 cheerleading camps per year
  — in 1985 30,000 aged 5-18 attended
    — largest camp was in Santa Barbara
      Calif. = 1,037 cheerleaders/4 days
  — U.S.A. teaches
    — stunts . . .communication skills . . . group
      dynamics . . . and spirit/attitude
      (Source: Iyer, Pico, ''Catching the Spirit,''
      Time, Aug. 12, '85, pp. 8-9)

(continued)

Notecards *(continued)*
"Yea for Cheerleading"

Male Cheerleaders #1

— Small percentage participate
  — U.S.A. camp in Santa Barbara in '85
    7 males present out of 1,037 people
      (Iyer, p. 8, Time mag.)

— At 1989 championships in Dallas in '89
    470 males present out of 4,230 people
      (Michael Neill and Ann Maier,
      ''Gimme a Yea!'' People Weekly,
      Jan. 23, '85, pp. 99-100)

Male Cheerleaders #2

— Things are changing
  — as cheerleading gets more complex and
    athletic, more strength is needed
      (pyramids, mounts, flips, carries)
  — MORE males are participating

(continued)

Notecards *(continued)*
"Yea for Cheerleading"

Competitions

– National championships
  – Dallas, Texas, 1989
    – 4,700 cheerleaders
    – representing 400 schools
    – groups were judged in eight divisions

Conclusion

– Qualities of cheerleader are many:
  – strength/flexibility/balance
  – enthusiasm
  – creativity
  – leadership
  – willingness to work with teammates

– Exciting, healthy
– Can develop skills used throughout life
  – be prosperous, positive att., and healthy

How to Write Reports

Master Plan
"Yea for Cheerleading"

I. Introduction

    A. Cheerleading provides:

        1. enthusiasm/encouragement

        2. sportsmanship

        3. entertainment/halftime

II. History

    A. Beginning

        1. Ancient people stood by roadsides cheering home warriors

    B. Mid-1800's

        1. 1860's during competitions among Ivy League colleges

    C. 1898—University of Minnesota

        1. first cheer: "Rah, Rah, Rah, Sis, Boom, Bah"

            a. first "yell marshal"—John Campbell

    D. 20th Century

        1. Today cheerl. is more athletic

            a. tumbling/gymnastics

            b. pyramids with flip dismounts

        2. Cheerl. is more dangerous

            a. 4,954 cheerl. emergencies in 1980

            b. 6,911   "   "   " 1986

              i. 40% increase

            c. *Example:* Janice Thompson

              i. killed in cheerl. stunt

        3. Argument over cheerleading

            a. Is it an activity (band/chorus)?

            b. Is it a sport?

              i. quote by Anderson

        4. Cheerleading needs rules/consistency

            a. quote by Weant

        5. Cheerl. needs rules/equal opportunity

            a. quote by Weant

        6. Cheerl. needs rules/safety

            a. sponsors should be trained

              i. quote by Butler

III. Cheerleading Camps

    A. Benefits

        1. Learn new tumbling skills

            a. mounts, stunts, dismounts

(continued)

Master Plan *(continued)*
"Yea for Cheerleading"

    2. Learn new chants/cheers
    3. Learn teamwork
    4. Learn social skills
       (meeting new people)
    5. Learn from best coaches in nation
B. Main Organization
    1. U.S.A.—United Spirit Association
      a. hosts nationwide cheerl. camps
        i. 82 camps per year
          a. largest in Santa Barbara, CA (1,037 cheerleaders)
      b. Promotes:
        i. new stunts
        ii. communication skills
        iii group dynamics
        iv. spirit/enthusiasm

IV. Male Cheerleaders

A. Small percentage participate
    1. 7 males out of 1,037 cheerleaders at Santa Barbara camp
    2. 470 males out of 4,230 cheerleaders at national championships in Dallas '89
B. But more joining all the time as cheerl. becomes more athletic, which requires strength

V. Competitions

A. National championships in Dallas '89
    1. Involved 4,700 cheerleaders
    2.   "   400 schools
    3. Cheerleaders judged in 8 categories

VI. Conclusion

A. Qualities of a cheerleader
    1. strength/flexibility/balance
    2. enthusiasm/spirit
    3. creativity
    4. leadership abilities
    5. willingness to work with teammates
B. Benefits of cheerleading
    1. healthy
    2. develops life skills

Final Report
"Yea for Cheerleading"
by Gena Sandberg

Tammy had never seen this kind of cheerleading. Along the sidelines stood ten girls in blue uniforms and behind them ten young men in blue slacks and white T-shirts, whose arms and chest bulged with muscles. At the first note of the school song, each girl leaped up onto the shoulders of her male partner, then hopped lightly into the air and stood on the palms of his hands eight feet in the air. One girl clapped and instantly all ten jumped straight up, twisted in midair, and landed in their partner's arms barely a foot off the ground. Now that's cheerleading, Tammy said to herself, thinking of how she would someday get on a university squad and do those same stunts.

Regardless of the type of stunts performed, cheerleading in all areas—junior high, high school, college, and professional sports—inspires enthusiasm and sportsmanship. Cheerleaders lead the crowd in chants and yells to help their team to victory. Cheerleaders also provide entertainment for the crowds; people enjoy their halftime shows as well as just watching them during the game.

Where it all began, no one really knows. There are a lot of questions but not as many answers. One theory suggested by Francis Shepard, author of *Go, Fight, Win!*, dates cheerleading back to ancient times when crowds of people lined the roads cheering their warriors home from battle. But cheerleading as we know it began in the 1860's when Ivy League colleges competed. By 1898, the University of Minnesota had a "yell marshal" named John Campbell who would rally the crowd with the official cheer, "Rah, Rah, Rah, Sis, Boom, Bah!" (Shepard, p. 1)

But cheerleading has changed. Today it has become a very strenuous activity, much like a sport. Cheerleaders use tumbling and gymnastics skills and a variety of rhythmic dance movements in their performances. They also reach great heights by building human pyramids. Most often, cheerleaders at the tops of those pyramids return to the ground by doing daring flips or jumps expecting to be caught by "spotters" on the ground.

This new approach has increased the element of danger in modern cheerleading. Every year there are thousands of injuries from cheerleading accidents. In 1980 the Consumer Products Safety Commission reported an estimated 4,954 hospital emergency visits due to cheerleading, and in 1986 that number rose to 6,911 emergencies—a 40 percent increase (Frankel, p. 56). The real tragedy is that some of those injuries turned out to be fatal.

(continued)

Final Report, page 2

An example is an accident that happened at North Dakota State University. Janice Thompson, a college senior who had been a cheerleader since her freshman year, was attempting to do a basic pike jump from a two-and-a-half-tier pyramid. She had done this stunt successfully many times before. However, this time she leaped and the experienced cheerleaders who were supposed to break her fall didn't have a chance. Thompson's head slammed against the floor. Her skull was fractured, and two days later she died.

Because of these kinds of dangers, it is thought by many that cheerleading should be considered an official sport. As it exists at the junior and senior high levels, cheerleading is considered an "activity" and thus it is not carefully regulated. There is no organized set of rules or limits for squads to follow. The question is: Is cheerleading an activity like marching band and chorus, or a sport like basketball and volleyball? Lisa Anderson, a former cheerleader at J. J. Pierce High School in Dallas, Texas, says that cheerleading is a sport. "It isn't just yelling and screaming anymore. Your hair is pulled back, and you're out there to sweat." (Frankel, p. 60)

High school athletic associations have been reluctant to accepting cheerleading as a sport; therefore no standard set of regulations exists. Teressa Weant, cheerleading coach at Lemon Bay High School in Englewood, Florida, explained the problem: "It's like basketball—you can't play if everyone has different rules." (Frankel, p. 60)

Because of this lack of national rules and regulations, rule-making has fallen to school districts and principals. This results in unequal opportunities for cheerleaders at different schools. Teressa Weant says, "We're a safety-minded school, so we're strict about rules. But when other squads come in and do three-tier pyramids, my girls all say, 'Why can't we do that?' If there was something set, then all the schools would have to abide." (Frankel, p. 60)

But some people feel that a standard set of rules and guidelines is not enough— cheerleading sponsors and coaches should be trained and qualified as well. Many believe it could help prevent accidents if the coach was trained to spot and teach proper methods. As it stands now, coaches and sponsors don't have to meet special requirements in most states to oversee cheerleading. "Some of the coaches are extremely talented people who believe in what they're doing. But there are others who look at cheerleading like a sponsor-type thing, meaning they do little more than make sure the kids are on the bus in time," says Melanie Butler, cheerleader coach at Huntington High School in Huntington, West Virginia. "The way cheerleading must go in the future is that coaches must be trained." (Frankel, p. 60)

(continued)

Final Report, page 3

Another way to improve cheerleading and reduce the risk of injury is for cheerleaders to attend cheerleading camps which are set up all over the country. Here participants learn everything from new stunts to how to work with new team members. Also, at the national camps, some of the best instructors in the nation provide training not just for the cheerleaders but for the sponsors and coaches as well.

A major sponsor of cheerleading camps, United Spirit Association (U.S.A.), promotes the teaching of communication skills, new stunts and workouts, group dynamics, and development of positive attitude or spirit. The organization hosts 82 camps per year from Montana to Hawaii for people from ages 5 to 18. In 1985, 30,000 people attended to brush up on cheerleading skills. In the largest encampment, which is located in Santa Barbara, California, 1,037 cheerleaders assembled for a 4-day seminar. Many who attended felt that their time at cheerleading camp was the best they've ever spent anywhere (Iyer, pp. 8–9).

But males aren't very well represented at these cheerleading camps because many males feel the whole sport is a "sissy" thing to do. In 1985 at the U.S.A. camp in Santa Barbara, for example, only 7 males were present out of a total of 1,037 people (Iyer, p. 8). And in Dallas, Texas, at the national championships in 1989, there were only 470 males out of 4,230 people attending (Neill, p. 99). But the image of cheerleading is changing, particularly on university campuses across the country where many squads are composed of equal numbers of young men and women. As cheerleading becomes more athletic, more gymnastics-oriented, it is predicted that the percent of males participating in the sport will increase in the future.

Whatever the future holds for cheerleading, one thing is sure—it can be an exciting, healthy, and rewarding activity that requires strength, enthusiasm, creativity, leadership abilities, and a willingness to work with others. It provides an excellent opportunity for young people to develop good physical and social qualities. And no one can doubt that those qualities are important not just in school or in athletics but also in all areas of life.

Works Cited

Frankel, Alison, "Is Cheerleading Getting Too Dangerous?" *Seventeen,* September 1987, pp. 56–60.

Iyer, Pico, "In California: Catching the Spirit," *Time* magazine, August 12, 1985, pp. 8–9.

Neill, Michael, and Anne Maier, "Gimme a Yea!" *People Weekly,* January 23, 1985, pp. 99–100.

Shepard, Francis, *Go, Fight, Win! The NCA Guide for Cheerleaders,* New York, Delacorte Press, 1981.

Works Consulted

Egbert, Barbara, *Action Cheerleading,* New York, Sterling Publishing Co., 1984.

Frankel, Alison, "Is Cheerleading Getting Too Dangerous?" *Seventeen,* Sept. 1987, pp. 56–60.

Iyer, Pico, "In California: Catching the Spirit," *Time* magazine, August 12, 1985, pp. 8–9.

Neill, Michael, and Anne Maier, "Gimme a Yea!" *People Weekly,* January 23, 1985, pp. 99–100.

Neill, Randy L., "Cheerleading," *The World Book Encyclopedia,* Volume 3, Chicago, World Book Inc., 1989.

Shepard, Francis, *Go, Fight, Win! The NCA Guide for Cheerleaders,* New York, Delacorte Press, 1981.